COUNTRY HU

DES WRIGHT is a Buckinghamshire man born and bred. His long association with Council Roadmen first began when, as a schoolboy playing marbles along the back-street gutters of his home town of Chesham, he met Jim – Council drain emptier and reclaimed marble supplier! Over the ensuing years, Jim and his contemporaries on the Chesham Urban District Council and Bucks County Council workforces were unknowingly acting out the scenes and sketches that were destined to play a major role in the 'Rustic Ramblings' stories.

Upon leaving school in 1952, Des began his working life on a mixed farm. However, in 1954, National Service intervened. Upon completion of this enforced duty, a brief spell on a poultry farm followed. He then entered the family business of Corn and Seed Merchants. It was his travels around the Buckinghamshire villages and backwaters in pursuit of his work, that was to bring him into contact with the Council Roadmen and many other interesting characters, who were to become his friends over the years. It is they – and Jim – who form the backbone of 'Rustic Ramblings' and 'Tap Room Tales'.

Des took over part of the family business when, in 1972, the old firm closed its doors for the last time. This enabled him to continue his travels around his usual haunts for the next 30 years and, at the same time, collect more material for further stories.

He married Molly in 1957 and they have two sons, Philip and Colin, and six grandchildren, amongst whom the general consensus of opinion is 'if you don't give us a mention, then we won't read the book!' So for Louise, Charlotte, Katie, Francesca, Jessica and Tom, the message is – read on!

Other interests include gardening, classical music, bird-watching, and walking the Yorkshire Dales. Although now past retirement age, he remains in full-time employment driving around the highways and byways meeting interesting people, always listening, hoping to glean a few snippets that will go towards making another story.

Elspeth Yule lives in Hightown on Merseyside. Although having many paintings and drawings to her credit, *Country Humour* is the first book Elspeth has illustrated.

Acknowledgements

Special thanks are due to Molly for her tolerance and help during the early stages of the development of this book in the 1970s and '80s, and for her continuing support

Special thanks also to Elspeth Yule, for her delightful line drawings

Thanks also to:

Peter Hawkes of Hawkes Design for his hard work and enthusiasm

Anne Noakes for the unenviable task of editing

Ian Freeman for the original photographs

Mel Barnett for help with photocopying
(courtesy of E.H.Smith Builders Merchants)

Chesham Musical Theatre Company
(formerly Chesham Light Opera Company)
for giving me the opportunity to air 'Rustic Ramblings'
on stage in the 1970s

DES WRIGHT'S

Country Humour

'Rustic Ramblings' & 'Tap Room Tales'

with illustrations by Elspeth Yule

This book is dedicated to the memory of my dear brother Bill, whose dry sense of country humour is legendary.

First published in Great Britain 2003 by Des Wright

ISBN 0-9545959-0-4

Typeset by Hawkes Design, Chesham

Printed by the Burlington Press at Foxton, Cambridge

Contents

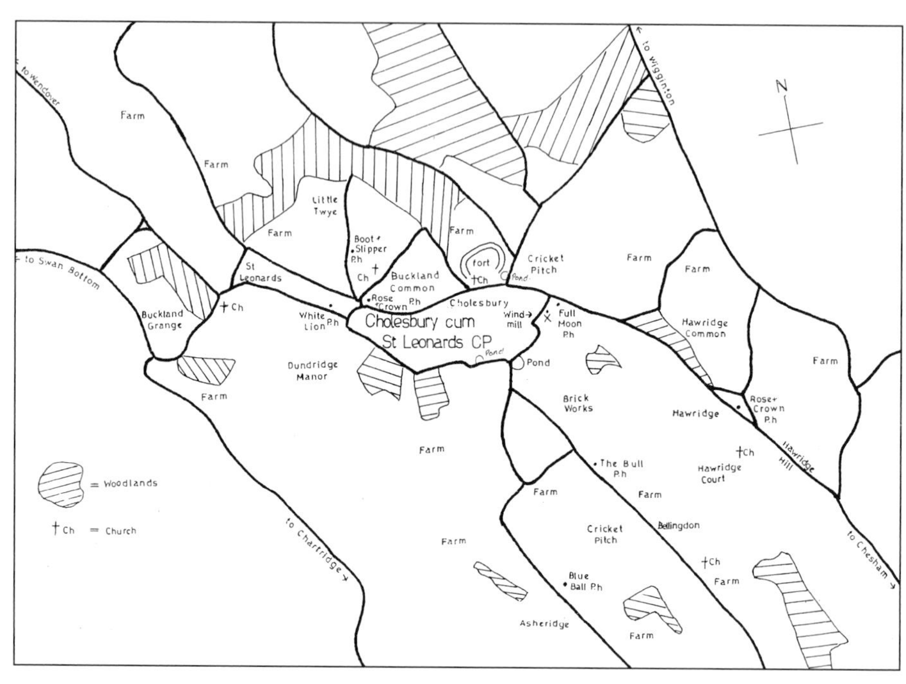

The setting for 'Rustic Ramblings' and 'Tap Room Tales'

Preface

THE MERE MENTION of rural England conjures up visions of green fields, woodlands, moorlands and picturesque villages with quaint thatched cottages and welcoming inns.

To most of us, there is nothing better than driving through the winding lanes of the English countryside, or walking along the many footpaths that wander through wood and farmland, taking in the wonderful scenery that this beautiful country of ours has to offer.

Today, modern transport gives us every opportunity to visit even the remotest parts of this lovely island, enabling us to experience at first hand the pleasures of the countryside. But, as is the case in most walks of life, the rural scene has undergone enormous change. Farming has now become such a highly mechanised industry over the last 40 years or so, that whereas there were quite probably as many as twenty or twenty-five men employed on a reasonably sized acreage, modern methods have drastically reduced that number to a mere handful. In some cases, where agricultural contractors are commissioned at peak times, it is now quite common to find just one man directly employed by the farmer on a full-time basis.

Mechanisation in the countryside, of course, is not confined to just the farming industry. County Councils, Local Authorities, and even the humblest of Rural Parish Councils, have also made great strides in that direction, with machines replacing employed labour for every conceivable aspect of roadside endeavour.

Mechanical diggers have replaced the pick and shovel, and are now employed for ditch digging and maintenance work. Tractor-mounted grass mowers and hedge trimmers consume acres of roadside verges and hedgerows, causing the old fashioned scythe and hedging billhook to become virtually redundant. Even that humblest of hand tools, the sickle, has finally succumbed to the highly acclaimed motorised strimmer – and how often has one been compelled to trail behind a monster, slow moving, left-hand drive sweeper lorry!

Unfortunately, progress has been achieved at considerable personal loss, depriving the village communities throughout the length and breadth of the country not only of many thousands of jobs, but also the very backbone of rural life – its people forced to leave the area by the acute lack of employment, and the spiralling cost of housing.

The deprivation of jobs in the countryside is to be forever mourned, as many of the rural occupations and crafts of yesteryear have all but disappeared. Some, however, still remain, such as the besom broom maker, the wheelwright, and the hedgelayer, to name but a few.

But for many, the demise of a once very familiar figure throughout rural England, is by far the greatest loss of them all. Unlike the besom broom maker and the wheelwright who still demonstrate their skills at agricultural shows up and down the country, the Council Roadman is, alas, extinct.

It has been both my privilege and pleasure to have been acquainted with many Council Roadmen, during the forty and more years spent travelling the lanes and back-waters of rural Buckinghamshire, and I have enjoyed many hours just listening to their wonderful tales of village life. Sadly, they are but a fond memory. Gone are the days when they were a familiar sight along the highways and byways of the English countryside, as much a part of the rural scene then, as the village green is today. Armed with shovel and broom, he pushed a green Bucks County Council wheelbarrow filled to capacity with the necessities for a day's work (the lunch bag was always the first item in!) and would set off for his alloted stretch of road at first light to do his bit for the community.

Roadside verges were always neat, tidy, and well mown – not by mechanical means as they are nowadays you understand, but kept so by one of the numerous pieces of essential equipment lying within the confines of his 'barrer', a tool known locally as a 'faggin' hook' – or sickle to give it its proper name, which was always honed to perfection with a carborundum sharpening stone – "what cost a tanner down at Brown's in the Broadway".

His stretch of road was spotless, and his ditches immaculate. Nobody dare throw away as much as a cigarette packet on his patch! He knew the brand each and every one of them smoked, how many they smoked, and when the packet was empty! If there did happen to be one lying about, woe betide you if you were the culprit, because he'd know straightaway whose it was, and he made sure everybody else knew as well. It didn't usually happen again!

But, of course, every job has its perks, and the job of Council Roadman was certainly no exception to the rule. In the halcyon days between the wars horses reigned supreme and, of course, where there are horses, there is bodily residue – to put a finer point on it! Bodily residue – hereinafter called 'orse minure – was a commodity highly sought after by all and sundry (you never put anything else on your rhubarb!). But rules are rules in every walk of life, and when on a Council Roadman's patch, they were strictly applied and strictly adhered to.

The rules were simple – whilst still in the 'orse, minure remained the property of its owner, but the minute that dropped onto the road, it was deemed Roadman's perks – and at a point of sale price of tuppence a barrerload, highly lucrative perks!

The Council Roadman played a crucial part in the day to day affairs of village life. Quite apart from his everyday job as custodian of the highways and all that entailed, there were numerous other positions that he held – Special Constable, fire-watcher, home guard, air-raid warden, fireman, assistant sexton and grave-digger, and part-time gardener – to mention just a few. Some of these, of course, were conscripted positions handed out during the second World War. He was also a fully paid up member of his local pub darts team – and sometimes even a parish councillor. If he wasn't the latter, then he could quite easily give you half a dozen good reasons as to why he wasn't – a certain fiery old party by the name of Miss Peacock being very definitely one that springs to mind!

Here was a man who, by the very nature of his work, came into contact with everyone connected with village life, from the retired Major General, down to the humble outdoor sanitorium bucket emptier. Nobody passed him by without a word or two about the weather, or some topic of village affairs – and who better, of course, to give passing strangers directions to anywhere in the village and beyond – and when he had done so, kept an eye on them (in his role as Special Constable) just to make sure that they were indeed just passing strangers, and not itinerant ne'er-do-wells! You can't be too careful y'know!

The calling of Council Roadman was one of the most important jobs in village life, trusted and respected by practically everyone in the community (there are always exceptions aren't there). A veritable mine of information, he was a man who knew just about everything that went on in the village. What he didn't know, he soon made it his business to find out! A man of countless tales and anecdotes willingly passed on to anyone who would care to listen.

Who better, then, to sit next to on the pub settle by the warmth of a real fire, than an authentic Council Roadman, his larynx well lubricated by a couple of pints of Old and Mild. Long since retired, of course, and the passage of time has taken its toll, but age is no barrier when it comes to retracing his steps back in time to the carefree days of long ago, back to the days when horsepower was measured with real horses – and if you wanted to go anywhere you always had a choice – you either walked, or you just didn't go!

But to know where and how these men used to work and spent their leisure hours (not that there were many of those) it is best to know first of all something of the area in which they operated. The map on page 8 gives you some indication of the areas they covered.

Hawridge, Cholesbury, Buckland Common, and St Leonards, are four villages situated high in the Chiltern Hills, four miles from the town of Chesham in the south, and about the same distance from Tring on the northern side. To the west lie the villages of Ashridge and Bellingdon, whilst due east stands the village of Wigginton.

The size and location of a village sometimes determined whether it should have its own roadman, or share him with an adjacent village. In many cases, the latter was deemed to be more practical, and therefore many roadmen found themselves working from boundary to boundary through two villages. This meant that, in effect, every road, lane, and byway within those confines, fell under his jurisdiction, which in most cases were quite considerable.

They weren't left to their own devices of course – the job wasn't that free and easy! All roadmen were under the direct control of the Buckinghamshire County Council Works Department (with the exception of Wigginton which lies in the County of Hertfordshire) and were regularly patrolled by a Road Foreman, who travelled the area on his motorcycle and sidecar. His brief was to set out the work each day, keep them all in order, and make sure everything ran as smoothly and as quietly as possible – with the exception of the 'wheelbarrers'! Always had squeaky wheels did 'wheelbarrers'. The Road Foreman's philosophy on Council Roadmen was quite simple – although you may not always be able to find them, if you wait around long enough, you are bound to hear them when they move – if they move that is! If only life were just as rewarding.

The tales in this book were related in the rich Buckinghamshire dialect, where H's at the beginning of words and G's at the end of words are not usually used, except when absolutely necessary, or used in all the wrong places as they very often are, and past and present tenses are regularly used in the same sentence.

They are reproduced here in almost the same context, the only difference being that all the H's and all the G's are included – mostly in all the right places!

The question is – are they authentic country tales, or are they just a figment of the storyteller's imagination?

Maybe a little enlightenment is required here . . .

. . . George was a carpenter for a local building firm. Very keen gardener was George, and at lunchtimes on the building site he came up with all sorts of home-grown produce – tomatoes, onions, lettuce, beetroot, carrots – you name it, George grew it – "all out of me own gardin!".

One particular time during the Summer harvest period, he would produce from his lunchbag a piece of cucumber about eight inches long, and proceed to eat it just as you or I would eat a raw carrot.

This went on for days on end, until at the end of the second week, one of his workmates just couldn't contain his curiosity any longer.

"George," he said, "every day now for the past fortnight, you've been bringing in a huge great lump of cucumber for your lunch – where on earth do you keep getting it from?" – or words to that effect!

"Ah!" said George, "you've bin itchin' to ask me that all week ain't yer – well – it's like this 'ere. I've got an 8 be 12 green'ouse at 'ome, and one night an old rat gnawed a great 'ole in the bottom corner of the door. There weren't nuthin' in there mind, so 'e wasted 'is time really. But that done me a good turn none the more for that, 'cause as you know, I always grows me own cucumbers – just the one plant mind – what I puts right in the far corner, and that fills the whole green'ouse. Well, d'you know, one of them there cucumbers, that's growed and that's growed and that's growed that quick, that's gorn twice round the green'ouse and back along the middle path, 'til at last that comed to the door, and d'you know – that's growed right through that rat 'ole clean as a whistle – and that's still a'growin' – so every mornin' afore I leaves for work, I walks down to the green'ouse, and I chops orf the bit what's growed through the rat 'ole, and brings it in 'ere for me lunch."

. . . True? – well, it's certainly true inasmuch that George had an 8 be 12 greenhouse, and used to grow all his own produce – particularly cucumbers! There's no doubt either, that an old rat gnawed a great hole in the bottom of the door – most greenhouses have got one of those!

As for the rest of the story – well, that's down to you the reader to judge for yourself, and arrive at your own conclusions.

Personally, I believe every last word of it! – but then, like the rest of the tales printed here, I've heard them all before – dozens of times!

So pull up your favourite chair – imagine it's the settle by the fireside in the public bar of the Rose and Crown on Hawridge Common – as it used to be years ago. Let's travel together, back in time to those halcyon days of yesteryear, and enjoy the stories of the Bucks County Council Roadmen . . .

Brusher Morley's wheelbarrer

Narrated by Brusher Morley

~ 1 ~ The Council Wheelbarrer

WHAT'S THAT you say? How did I first come to get the job of Council Roadman? Ha, you may well ask – but it were quite by accident really.

It all started when I called into the Council yard one day – that's over fifty year ago now. Blimey! – did I work there that long? But then, I suppose I must have done – I got a gold watch for it! Anyway, that's neither here nor there is it? I only called in there to see if they'd got ne'ery an old Council wheelbarrer what they didn't want any more. I needed one pretty bad y'see, on account as my old one fell apart up at the allotment. Well, it weren't surprising really, that weren't in very good condition when I had it years ago. That had been handed down, y'know, from my old Dad, and his old Dad before him – so that had been about a few years!

Anyway, I calls in the Council yard just on the off chance they might have one going spare – well, if you don't ask you don't get do you? So I sees a chap standing in there, and I asked him which one of them wus foreman. Well, you can't tell when they're all standing still can you – and d'you know, I can remember exactly what he said, just like that wus yesterday . . .

"Here mate," I says, "have you got ne'ery an old Council wheelbarrer laying about what you don't want?"

"Oh ar," he says, "there's one over there," he says, "you can have that – we don't use them at all these days."

So I says "No," I says, "they never used them much in the old days neither!"

So he says "Well, how are you going to get it home then?"

So I says "Well, I thought I might push it!"

He says "You'll be careful when you go out of the yard then won't you mate, only Council wheelbarrers ain't used to being pushed y'know – and don't you let the old Road Foreman see you pushin' it."

"Why not?" I says.

"Well," he says, "he ain't never seen one moving before!"

I wus just going out of the yard, when the old Road Foreman comed across.

"Hi!" he shouted, "where d'you think you're a'going with that there old Council wheelbarrer?"

"I'm taking it home," I says.

"Oh no you ain't," he says, "if I see you push that barrer out of this 'ere yard, there'll be trouble."

So I says "Oh?" – and he says "Ar!" – so I does no more, I turns the barrer round and I pulls it out back'ards first. Ar, that had him!

"You're a smart feller," he says, "how would you like to work on the Council?"

"Go on with you," I says, "why should I be the first one ever to do a thing like that!"

"Do you know anything about Council work?" he says.

So I says "No," I says.

"Well, that's alright then," he says, "because there ain't nobody here that knows either! Now then" he says, "do you know how to use a shovel?"

"Well – no," I says.

So he says, "What about a broom then?" I told him I didn't know much about them either.

So he says, "Well . . . well, what can you do then?"

So I says, "Well . . . I can roll a fag one-handed."

He says, "You're just the chap we been a'looking for – you can be Foreman!"

"Hold on," I says, "what's the money like then?"

"That's 2d an hour," he says, "that's the standing rate for Council Roadmen."

"Oh?" I says, "how much is it if they move about then?"

"Well, I don't know," he says, "we've never had any here what do that yetawhile!"

I says, "You don't want me," I says, "how many chaps work on the Council?"

"About half of them," he says.

"Oh – alright," I says, "but I shall have to put me bike somewhere where it ain't likely to get pinched."

"I got just the place for that," he says, "we can put that in the Council toolshed, nobody ever goes in there." – And that wus it, I got the job as Council Roadman, just like that! – and do you know, I've had that old wheelbarrer ever since, and that's still in good nick. Of course, that's a proper old 'un y'know. You can tell that by the writing on it – B.C.C. – that's Before Christ Come – so you can tell it's a real old 'un!

Old Percy Lamkin wus pushing that when he had his accident y'know, a long while before I had it. He got knocked down by one of them there new fangling motor cars, and broke both his legs. But you can't keep a good man down for long y'know. He wus back at work next morning good as new. Ha – a six inch nail in each leg, hammered right up into his bottom, and he wus as right as ninepence! 'Course, old Percy wus alright, he never hurt his-self. When that knocked him over, he landed headfirst in the wheelbarrer. The old Road Foreman says that wus the first time that old barrer had been filled up for a fortnight!

Not like the time poor old Tommer Maybank got his-self knocked over. He wus turnip pulling y'know – in the same field as Charley Buckley kept Bunty, his old Billy goat. He wus the bestest bunter Charley had ever had y'know. Hoor, he couldn't half bunt them. 'Course, every time old Tommer bent down, he got his-self bunted in the backside. Well, after going headfirst into his pile of turnips for the umpteenth time, he wus getting a bit fed up with it y'know. In the end, he scrambles up and hollers out "Right Billy goat Buckley, I'll have you the next time!" Ar, and he did too! Next time Bunty come a'galloping up, old Tommer swings round and fetches him one right on top of his head with his turnip chopper and knocks him out – stone cold!

"Gotcher!" shouted old Tommer at the top of his voice, "now bunt yer beggar." – only of course, he never said beggar.

But he couldn't half swear y'know. Hoor, he wus the bestest swearer we ever had. Well, they do say he knowed more swear words than what the old Vicar did – which ain't bad when you comes to think about it. Well, I mean to say, the old Vicar went to one of them there theomagical places – y'know, where they teach them all about them there sort of things – but old Tommer, well, he had to learn his all by his-self!

He used to do a few odd jobs in the village be times y'know. The old Vicar says to him one time as how they could do with some more turves for the churchyard.

"We can't afford any new 'uns Tommer," he says, "see if you can get some old 'uns from somewhere."

So Tommer sticks a notice up on the church notice-board – and d'you know what that said? Well, I'll tell you...

WANTED
A few old sods to lay in the churchyard.
About 50 or 60 would do.
Must be in good condition. Apply within.

He'd just put it up, when along comed old Percy Lamkin a'pushing his wheelbarrer. Well, he never walks anywhere y'know. He looks at the notice, then at old Tommer, then he says, "Can't see you doing much good with that, Tommer," he says.

"Well, why not?" says Tommer.

"Stands to reason," says Percy, "most of the old sods in this here village are a lot older than that, and besides," he says, "when that's time for them to come to this here place, they ain't going to be in very good condition neither."

I mind the time we had a Rummage Sale in the village hall up there on the Common. That wus run by the Women's Institute – y'know, where they sells yer nearly new cakes, and tea made out of evacuated milk, stirred all up with a spoonful of castrated sugar.

I takes me wheelbarrer to all the Rummage Sales. Handy things wheelbarrers at

Rummage Sales y'know. You just has to fill it up with nice fresh 'orse minure – what you pick up off the road on the way – and that guarantees you first place in the queue every time. That never fails!

Charley Buckley goes to all the Rummage Sales as well y'know. He reckons that's the only time you can fumble through women's underwear without getting yourself into trouble. But when I gets in there poor old Charley wus in trouble. He'd just grabbed hold of Miss Peacock's drawers from off the underwear stall. Well, they weren't exactly Miss Peacock's. The trouble wus, her and Charley had both clarred hold of them at the same time, and neary one of them would let go. Why should they? They wus fair game. Charley wanted them for his daughter to put in her big bottom drawer – and Miss Peacock just wanted them to put in her big bottom!

Well, there they wus a'pulling and a'tugging, until at last Miss Peacock hollers out, "you let go of my drawers Charley Buckley, you're always the same at Rummage Sales, always grabbing at my drawers!"

Well, that done it! Old Charley went as red as a beetroot y'know. Well, he weren't like that, him being a regular churchman and all.

"Here you are!" he hollers, letting go of the drawers "you'd better take them – but you make sure you wear them when you comes to Harvest Festival."

"And why should I do that?" she says.

"Well," says Charley, "I reckon when you got them on, all will be safely gathered in."

"Ooooh!" she says, "I'm glad I ain't your missus," she says, "if I wus married to you I'd give you rat poison."

"Yes," says Charley, "and if I wus married to you I'd take it!"

"Never mind Charley," I says, "how d'you like a pair of these fancy coloured ones like the young girls wear these days?"

"Well, they're alright," he says, "but they're like the beer glasses down at the Rose and Crown – they looks a lot better when there's something inside them."

He wus still smarting when he went out through the door, but I thought at the time – knowing Charley Buckley as well as I did – that it wouldn't be very long before he got his own back . . . and I wus right!

I always had a big sack on my wheelbarrer handles. That keeps your hands nice and warm y'know – especially when that's part filled with nice warm 'orse minure. Only somebody pinched it one time, so I asked Charley Buckley if he'd got one or two to spare from out his Windmill.

"I'll be along by the village hall directly," I says, "the Women's Institute are having a "Keep the Village Tidy" meeting on the green – I've got to sweep up the mess afterwards."

"Righto," he says, "I'll be there shortly."

Well, when I gets along there, all the old girls from the Institute are standing round in a bunch a'listening to Miss Peacock. Just then, Charley Buckley comes along with them old sacks in his horse and cart. He wus just a'going to say something, when Miss Peacock starts orf at us.

"Ha!" she says, "if our Roadman did as much sweeping, as he does talking to Charley Buckley, we wouldn't have need of this meeting."

"Right!" says Charley, "I'll have her," he says, and he chucks that bundle of bags right into my wheelbarrer, then says to me, just loud enough so's they could all hear:-

"I understand you wants a big old bag to warm your hands with old mate," he says. "Well, there's 5 or 6 old bags there what'll do you a good turn, but right in the middle of that bunch you'll find a big old haybag with a wide mouth and a large bottom. You get your hands round that," he says, "I bet that'll keep 'em warm alright."

Well, that had her. I thought she were going to burst, but before she could say anything, old Charley got in first.

"Ah well, Miss Peacock," he says, "you ain't such a bad sort really – how would you like a big sack to keep you nice and warm when you're out driving that pony and trap of yours?"

Well, she melted straight away!

"Oooh I say, thank you very much Mr Buckley," she cooed, "that would be very nice."

So old Charley reaches in the back of his cart, and fetches out a huge great sugar sack.

"There you are," he says, "try that for size" and he fixes it up round her middle with a bit of old binder twine.

Well, we had to laugh y'know. Old Charley had certainly got his own back for the Rummage Sale drawers alright, because there wus some writing across the sack on Miss Peacock's backside y'know, and that read:-

2 CWT OF THE BESTEST QUALITY.
UNTOUCHED BY HUMAN HANDS.

Ha, that don't take long to get your own back does it!

But all's well that ends well, that's what I say, and everybody went home happy in the end.

I never thought I'd see the day when Miss Peacock had a good laugh, but she joined in with everyone else that day. Well, she thought she better had, seeing as how her W.I. ladies were all a'busting their sides at whatever it wus they could see on the sack and she couldn't. In the end, they all walked back for tea at the Institute, with tears of laughter streaming down their faces, and Miss Peacock still wearing that huge great sack, tied round her middle with a bit of old binder twine. It wus a sight I shall never forget!

As for Charley Buckley, well, he wus more than happy, on account as he had more than made up for the loss of them there Rummage Sale drawers by getting one over on Miss Peacock, though I had no doubts whatever that Miss Peacock would soon be on the warpath again, just as soon as she took that old sack off, and see'd what wus written on it spread all across her backside. But I expect that's a few stories further on yetawhile.

And me? Well, I wus very happy. I'd just got one of the bestest jobs in the whole village, a wonderful new B.C.C. wheelbarrer, a plentiful supply of nice thick sacks to keep me hands warm in the winter – and as I wus walking home, I filled up me barrer with enough 'orse minure for me bean trench up at the allotment.

What more could a chap ask for out of life . . . Right, that's that then – I'm off home now. No, no – I ain't really got time to tell you another tale tonight – what's that you say, another pint? Well now, that's different altogether ain't it! Just one more mind, then I really shall have to go. Nice drop o'stuff this Old and Mild ain't it. What's that you say? Have I seen the Girl Guides camp on Hawridge Common? Yes – yes, I have, and I'm steering well clear of it – and so would you too, if you had been through what me and Billy Puddick went through, when we got ourselves a'tangled up with old Miss Peacock and her Girl Guides. Hor! What! You don't know half what goes on with that lot! And I'll tell you something else and all – them old badges what they wears on their arms and that – Interest Badges they are y'know. Ha! – you don't get them as raffle prizes at W.I. meetings. You have to earn them beggars I can tell you! Me and old Billy was humiliated, abused, and damn nigh drowned a'winning ours!

I'll tell you all about it shall I? We've got a little while afore closing time ain't we? Yes, I thought we had! Well . . .

Brusher Morley's story continues on page 26

~ 2 ~
The Waterer's Apprentice

FREDDIE MAYNARD, the Water Bailiff, was up at Willum's Farm back in the Springtime, measuring the depth of the dew pond, with his apprentice, young George Puddick.

He wasn't using young George as a measuring stick you understand, although he sometimes thought he ought to. He reckoned as how "a damn good ducking would do 'im a power of good."

Freddie had already got a perfectly good measuring stick, Water Board approved and British Standards Institute kite marked and all that, so, for the time being at least, young George the Waterer's Apprentice was reasonably safe, but Freddie was keeping his options open on that one.

Unfortunately, this particular morning, "he'd gorn and left the blessed thing at 'ome", or so he thought, so he asked old Willum, who was leaning on the fence watching proceedings, "if he knowed just how deep the pond wus."

Now there's quite a few bodies about as ought to know how deep Church Farm dewpond is, but without a shadow of doubt, there's nobody better qualified than old Willum. He's in a class of his own. After all, he's a time-served apprentice in the profession of falling into dewponds and the like, and he's "felled into this one on the way 'ome from the Rose and Crown more times than I could ever think of remembering."

In fact, he can tell you the depth of all the ponds within a two mile radius of Church Farm. He doesn't miss many out during the course of a drinking week – and not just approximate measurements either – he knows exactly how deep. He certainly hasn't the need of a Water Board Approved Measuring Stick, that's for sure.

He's got letters behind his name for falling into dewponds has Willum, or any other pond for that matter. Letters that, when strung together, make up words, like 'Damn and Blast the Beggaring Ponds' or 'Jam and Butter it' – and all such words as that. You name 'em, he's said 'em.

As for Freddie Maynard, well . . . he's a good old boy is Freddie. Do anything for you y'know, and he'd give you his last penny, but in his capacity as a Water Bailiff, he becomes quite officious at times, gets carried away with the importance of the job, and then starts throwing his weight about.

. . . And that particular day back in the Spring was one such time . . .

"Well," replies old Willum, in answer to Freddie's enquiry, "the depth varies a bit, but that's generally round about, or just below me knees when I'm . . ."

"Right," interrupts Freddie, in his best officious voice, "I don't want nothing that's generally round about – in future, I shall want you to tell me exactly when the depth varies, and by how much. Do you understand?"

"Oh ar," says old Willum, "I understand – you need to know about it straight-away, but I think you should let me finish what I wus a'goin' to tell yer about how deep . . ."

"Yes, yes that's right," says Freddie, a touch impatiently, fetching out his official Water Board Approved Notebook, and licking the end of his pencil, in a very official and workmanlike manner, not taking a blind bit of notice as to what old Willum was saying. "I need to know straight-away – now then, let's get on with the job. Seeing as how that's only about two foot deep, according to your knees, and bearing in mind that my Water Board Approved Waterproofed Wellie-Waders are all of three foot tall, I shall walk out to the middle of this 'ere pond, without any fear of getting me feet wet."

"Just as you loike," says old Willum, still a'leaning on the fence.

Well, Freddie steps into the pond and, do you know, he was all there one minute – and all gone the next. Disappeared under a great mass of frog spawn and Jenny Green Teeth – Water Board Approved Waterproofed Wellie-Waders an' all – just like that there.

He couldn't stand up to start with, he was too busy slipping and sliding on all that there frog spawn. Under he went again, got his head out of the water for the second time, stood up briefly, then did a repeat performance. He finally managed to stand up at the third attempt, up to his neck in stagnant dewpond water coughing up Jenny Green Teeth, and spitting out frog spawn.

He was as wild as an 'awk y'know, and that didn't help matters one little bit, when old Willum asked him if he'd managed to keep his feet dry. He started leading off at old Willum something terrible after that. He carried on alarming for about five minutes, and only stopped then on account as he ran out of swear-words. By the sound of him, they reckoned he must have borrowed a few of the letters that old Willum's got behind his name – either that, or he'd fell into a few ponds in his time and learned them all by himself.

Either way, young George Puddick was getting a first class grounding in best Water Board language during the first year of his apprenticeship, that's for sure.

Old Willum reckoned that it was a waste of time and money sending him to day release classes after that. It was Willum's considered opinion that young George learned more in those five minutes than they could ever teach him at college.

"Hoi!" shouts a dripping wet Freddie, directing his gaze at old Willum, who was still leaning on the fence. "Hoi! – what's your game then? You told me it only comed up to your knees."

"That's right," says old Willum, "so it does, when I'm sat on me 'orse. I tried to tell yer earlier on, but you wouldn't . . ."

. . . "*When you're sat on your 'orse? – When you're sat on your 'orse?*" bellows Freddie, interrupting again, "what sort of an idiot are you then?"

"A dry'un," says old Willum, and moving away from the fence, reveals a notice-board behind him what says:

DANGER
FAIRLY DEEP DEWPOND

"A nice and dry'un," he says, "and one as can read well enough not to go jumping into fairly deep dewponds – but I'll give credit where credit's due," he says, "that didn't take you very long to find out how much the depth varies, did it?"

"Never mind that," cries Freddie, "how am I supposed to measure the depth of this 'ere dewpond, with no measuring stick, and an idiot like you giving me misleading information?"

"Easy," says old Willum, "you just measure the distance from your neck to my knees."

"Oh, right," says Freddie, reaching for his notebook as it floated past on the water, although for obvious reasons, not bothering to lick the end of his pencil this time, "why didn't you say that in the first place – maybe we're gettin' somewhere at last – so what is the measurement then?"

"From where I'm standin'?" says old Willum, "I reckon that's 'bout 24 foot – give or take a few inches – and from where you're standin'? – well, that ain't far orf from being near enough the same is it, so let me see – altogether, that'll be exactly 48 foot – more or less. On the other 'and," he says, "seein' as how you're water orientated, being a Water Board Approved Water Bailiff an' all that, and really dedicated to the job by being submerged up to your neck in the stuff just now, by the simplest of calculations, 48 foot works out to exactly 8 fathoms – in the bestest of nautical terms."

"48 foot?" cries Freddie, as he clambered out of the pond, "8 fathoms? – that can't be right."

"Course it ain't right," butts in young George suddenly, who, up until now, had just been an innocent bystander watching the events unfold, "it ain't very deep at all across the other side."

". . . and how do you figure that out?" says Freddie, trying to regain his composure and sense of authority in front of Willum, whilst at the same time struggling with his apprentice, who was trying to remove one of the Water Board Approved Waterproofed Wellie-Waders from his governor's leg in best riding boot fashion.

"Well, it can't be," cries young George, "anybody can see that – it only comes halfway up them ducks."

"Is that so?" says Freddie "how would you like to test out your theory?" – and before young George could utter any sort of reply, a Water Board Approved Waterproofed Wellie-Wader planted itself firmly on his backside at great speed, and he found himself putting his theory into immediate practice, the result of which left him in no doubt whatsoever, that whilst ducks could sit quite comfortably on top of Church Farm dewpond, he most certainly could not.

"Well, I'll tiggle orf now," says old Willum, "seein' as how you two 'ave got the job well in 'and." As he sotchells off across the meadow, he turns round and calls back to Freddie.

"By the way – don't forget your Water Board Approved Measuring stick will yer."

"How d'you mean?" replies Freddie, "don't forget it – I already did, I left it at 'ome this morning."

"No you didn't," says Willum "it's over there, leaning agin that sign what says: Beware Fairly Deep Water – exactly where your 'prentice left it yesterday."

Young George, who by this time was just climbing up out of the pond, took one look at the expression on Freddie's face, and jumped straight back in again, striking out through the frog spawn and Jenny Green Teeth, heading furiously towards the beckoning refuge of the opposite bank.

When old Willum finally sotchelled away from the scene, young George found himself under severe bombardment from a sustained aerial attack, expertly aimed by Freddie Maynard, using ammunition consisting of two pairs of Water Board Approved Waterproofed Wellie-Waders, packed to the gunnels with a decidedly unfriendly cocktail, consisting of Jenny Green Teeth, frog spawn, and stagnant dewpond water.

But the ultimate weapon was a deadly harpoon, cleverly disguised as a Water Board Approved Dewpond Measuring Stick, homed in on its target with unerring precision and dexterity, a unique art undoubtedly derived and perfected over the years during disputes with errant apprentices.

Old Willum reckoned as how that was the bestest use of a dewpond measuring stick he's ever likely to see.

. . . And d'you remember that phrase as coined by Freddie Maynard? – when he said of young George "that a damn good ducking would do 'im a power of good?" . . .

Well, that certainly did – because d'you know, young George has never mislaid a Water Board Approved Dewpond Measuring Stick not from that day 'til this.

. . . Who, in their right mind, would ever volunteer to be a Water Board Approved Waterer's Apprentice?

~ 3 ~
Three Ancient Baden-Powellers

THAT ALL STARTED way back one Summer-time, when the Cholesbury-cum-St Leonards Girl Guides had their Annual Camp up there on Hawridge Common.

140 of them there were – with old Miss Peacock in charge! She never had no help y'know. Well, she never needed none, she could manage that lot alright! Well, as you know, she runs the W.I. meetings all by herself. If you can do that, then I reckon 140 Girl Guides must be easy. She soon sorts out any troubling argifyers y'know. She irons them out the same way she irons her knickers – she takes a'hold of them by the legs, gives them a good shake to get rid of the wind, then sits on them! Ha, that sorts them out alright. They ain't got no wind left to argify with after that. But she never has no trouble y'know, leastways she didn't . . . up until then!

It wus old Billy what started it all. Me and him had been stood there for about 40 minutes waiting for the Full Moon to open, and we'd been watching these here Girl Guides struggling with their tents for quite some time, when old Billy just happened to mention – quite on purpose so's they could all hear – that he wus in the South African War in 1899, a'fighting them old Boers alongside Lord Baden-Powell and all the other heroes, at the 217 day defence of Mafeking – and he just happened to mention at the same time, that Lord Baden-Powell himself helped him put their tents up!

Well, that done it! Miss Peacock shouted out one sharp word of command, and before we knowed what wus happening, there we wus knee-deep in Girl Guides.

"I dunno," shouts old Billy, as we were struggling underneath 30 or 40 of them, "that story about Mafeking has earned me hundreds of pints over the years down at the Rose and Crown. Up here," he says, "you just get sat on!"

"Righto girls!" bellows old Miss Peacock, "drag their clothes off, get these uniforms on them, and let's get them enrolled a bit quick – we got some tents to put up and all y'know!"

Well, you never see'd anything like it. Four of them clarred me trousers off, three more had me shirt, two had me boots, and Miss Peacock had what wus left – which at my time of life, weren't very much! Well, things don't last forever do they!

But you should have seen the pair of us, dressed up in these here Girl Guides' uniforms – about to become the laughing-stock of every public bar from here to

Wigginton. We've never ever lived it down I can tell you! But where was I? Oh yes, I remember . . .

"Well," says old Billy, "that's that then, we've been press-ganged into the Girl Guides right enough, but we'll never make it into the Boy Scouts that's for sure – we just failed their first Commandment!"

"Oh!" I says, "what's that then?"

"Why," says old Billy, "Be Prepared, of course. If we had a been prepared," he says, "we'd have got away before that lot jumped on us."

Poor old Billy. He looked a bit worse for wear after being sat on by all them young girls and Miss Peacock. Well, 25 stone and rising fast she wus y'know. Billy said that wus just like Mafeking all over again – only much worse! He said that wus a good job Miss Peacock weren't fighting for them old Boers at Mafeking then. He reckoned if she'd a'sat on our chaps there, why, they never would've got the seige lifted.

I ain't never seen a seige y'know – but according to that, whatever it is, that must be pretty heavy!

Billy said he didn't mind the young girls a'sitting on him, although he would have enjoyed it a lot more if he'd been a few years younger – but old Miss Peacock, well, she ain't none too careful y'know, especially with her hands! Hor! She knowed where to put them alright – they never needed no guiding I can tell you!

Billy said the last time Miss Peacock got her hands on him was during the war y'know, when they reckoned to be fire-watching up there at Charley Buckley's Windmill. Ha, them two never did much fire-watching I can tell you – but things got pretty hot between them up there none the more for that. They wus both a lot younger in them days, so of course, things were a bit different then, well, they weren't putting up tents for a start!

"Right!" says old Miss Peacock, "now we come to the swearing-in bit." They calls it enrolment really, but what with old Billy's language being a bit hot, they reckoned that swearing-in wus about right.

"Being a good Guide," she says to me and old Billy, "means keeping a good moral code, being a good villager, chivalrous behaviour – and skill in h'outdoor activities."

"Ha! – old Billy's good at the last one," I says, "you ask Mrs Turvey about the time when him and her wus on top of that strawrick, up there at Church Farm back in 1926."

"1926?" says old Billy. "That weren't Mrs Turvey that time, that wus . . ." and before he could say another word, Miss Peacock give him a swift kick on the shins, and told him to keep his mouth shut! I had to laugh, ha!

"And for your information," she says to me, "it weren't a strawrick in 1926, it were nice soft medder hay!"

"Oh?" I says.

"Yes," she says, "it were prickly old straw in 1927 – I remember that," she says, "because I wus . . ." and she stopped, just like that there, and went as red as a beetroot! Well, that finished off the swearing in ceremony, so we all troops off across the common down to the campsite.

"Now then," says Miss Peacock, "let's see about these here tents – what do you know about guy ropes?"

"Well – nothing," I says, "I don't even know the chap."

"No, no!" she says, "guy ropes are bits of string what holds the tent up, along with larch poles."

"Oh!" I says, "I knows him."

"Knows who?" she says.

"Why – Arch Poles," I says, "he lives up there agin . . ."

"No, no!" she says, "larch poles, larch poles – they goes in the middle and props up the tent."

"Well I never!" I says, "there ain't a lot of difference really is there?"

"How do you mean?" she says.

"Well," I says, "larch poles props up the tent on the camping ground, and Arch Poles props up the bar at the Rose and Crown."

After that, I wus pushed up the stepladder to fasten the top of the tent. I'd just got to the top step, when in comed the old Vicar, in his capacity as Honorary Guider. He stood right underneath the ladder, peered up me skirt and says: "Hello, got a new Guider then? I ain't seen that one before!"

It wus just at that very minute that Billy won his first Interest Badge, and the old Vicar lost two of his, because I wus just about to hit the Vicar over the head with me mallet, when old Billy grabbed it from out of me hand, and Miss Peacock straightway awarded him a Red Triangle Badge for Accident Prevention and at the same time took away the Vicar's Observer's Badge – for not being able to tell the difference between a him and a her when one of them is up a ladder!

"I dunno," says old Billy, "there's summat wrong here somewhere. If our old Vicar can't tell the difference between a chap guide and a girl guide after looking up your skirt – particular up a ladder – then either he's going blind or else you ain't the man you reckon out to be!"

The second badge the Vicar lost wus the Stargazer's Badge. He would've won that one easy y'know, if Billy Puddick hadn't have pinched my mallet!

Well, we got all the tents up after a struggle, and then Miss Peacock gets all the girls lined up across there by the village pond, ready for inspection by the District Conditioner!

"Come on you two!" she bellows at me and old Billy, as we stood at the edge of the pond a'watching them young girls, "fall in!".

"You what?" says old Billy.

"Fall in!" she bellows again – louder than ever. "Fall in, and be quick about it!" and she give old Billy an almighty shove, just to help him on his way a bit. Well, it did that alright, because Billy lurched into me and knocked me cap off, causing it to fall into the water. I wouldn't have minded that on its own, I could've fished that out of the pond alright – but as old Billy wus a'falling he grabbed a'hold of me skirt to try to stop his-self! That comed down round me ankles – I started falling as well – and with one h'almighty splash, the pair of us followed me cap into the pond, just as the District Conditioner comed walking across!

I tried to get away before we fell in, but that ain't half a job trying to move quick when you've got a Girl Guide skirt round your ankles, ain't it? Well, you wouldn't know about that would you. I ain't never tried it before either! The nearest I come to it wus one time when the siren went off during the war. I mind I wus down the garden at the time, in me old h'outdoor sanitorium. I had me trousers round me ankles then. I mind I jumped up from the seat as that went off and tried to turn round a bit quick – only I caught me feet in me braces! As I fell over, I banged me head on the door, and finished up losing me pipe in the h'outdoor sanitorium bucket! I didn't get that back until six weeks later, when old Henery Padfield comed round with the Council tumbril and emptied the bucket – and dang me if that old pipe hadn't gone out!

On top of that, I had to pay old Henery a sixpenny search fee – and that was a reduced rate on account I wus a Council employee!

Well, there we wus – the pair of us wallowing in the water. I went under three or four times a'looking for me cap and, at the same time, trying to put me skirt back on. Well, that ain't none too easy y'know – especially when you're up to your armholes in duck pond water. You can't get your legs in y'know, when that keeps on floating about.

But you ought to have seen them Girl Guides! They wus a'shouting, and they wus a'clapping, and they wus a'cheering for all they wus worth – all 140 of them! Dear oh pray – what a row they kicked up, ten times worse than a W.I. meeting! In the end, old Billy grabs me by the scruff of me neck, and drags me to the bank.

"Hold on a minute," I says. "Hold on! I ain't found me cap yetawhile!"

"Never mind that," says old Billy, "out you come. I've just about had enough of this game." So we both clambers out and sat on the duck shed to drain. Old Billy, well, he wus as wild as an hawk y'know – but the District Conditioner, she wus as pleased as Punch!

"Well done! Well done!" she says, a'shaking Billy by the hand, "I've never seen a finer bit of life savery in all me born days! What an hero!" And she gives Billy a great big kiss – and out comed a great big bagful of Interest Badges!

For his heroic deed in saving me from the murky water, she give old Billy two Rescuer's Badges – she said that wus worth more than one!

For keeping the Girl Guides amused, she give both of us our Entertainer's Badge, and for pushing both of us into the pond Miss Peacock got two days tater-peeling!

'Course, the story got round all the villages in no time at all – as to how old Miss Peacock got two months for trying to murder both of us – and how old Billy fought her off with his bare hands, and then dived into the village pond into 20 foot of water in front of thousands of cheering Girl Guides to rescue his bestest pal from a watery grave – and how the District Conditioner give him the V.C. and bar for his most gallant deed!

Old Billy did alright out of that y'know. Well, he downed more pints in the first fortnight when the story got about, than he had in all the years put together for the story about Mafeking. He said that's a pity we never joined the Girl Guides years ago. I said it's a good job we didn't – I can't afford to lose too many caps. I never did find it y'know – come the next breeding season, I reckon them old ducks on the pond used that for a nest . . .

. . . Lawk-a-massey-me! – is that the time already? Ah well, it don't really matter when you're talking about the old times does it? I can see we shall have to make this story-telling a regular thing. Let me see . . . have you ever heard tell about Samuel Mortlock's wonderful Fire Brigade? – No? – Well now, that does surprise me! You must have heard all about Freddie Maynard the Water Bailiff then, I know? You haven't? Dear me! – You have led sheltered lives ain't you! What about the time that old Dawdling Bug comed a'whistling over the top of Charley Buckley's Windmill then? No? – Well! I thought everybody heard that!

All I can say is then, I reckon you're in for a treat when you comes in here again.

What's that you say? How often do I gets in here? Well, I think I can safely say I ain't missed a Friday night for 50 year or more. Old Miss Peacock would have you believe I lives here all the time, but I reckon I just bides awhile.

Anyways, I'm off home now – and I'll see you all next time. Oh, and thanks for the Old and Milds – they wus beautiful!

So long.

Brusher Morley's story continues on page 47

~ 4 ~
The Parable of the Fivepence Ha'penny Talent

THIS IS A REMARKABLE story as told to me, word for word, in the Tap Room of the Rose and Crown. You have it as I had it – complete and unabridged. It is the story of a mission – a mission undertaken by one man against seemingly overwhelming odds – but, as he discovered, with the Lord on your side, a little bit of Faith, and being in the right place at the right time, anything is possible . . .

Church Farm – ah, the name alone conjures up wonderful memories of bygone years, and transports them to the very front of one's mind.

A magical place was Church Farm. Farms always are when you're just a kid aren't they? It was alive with the comings and goings of such a rich variety of rustic characters, the likes of which we shall never see again.

It lies up there beyond the further most boundary of the cricket ground, up the cart track, then 200 yards beyond the village pond, with the church amply visible from the confines of the rick-yard. It's always been there, all 147 acres of it, ever since anybody can remember. They do say it never was anywhere else.

Willum Trottwood's family have worked Church Farm for hundreds of years, and he's that ancient himself, folks do say he's been there all the time, but nobody really knows for sure. The old Vicar called to see him one day, and during the course of their conversation, asked old Willum if he'd lived at Church Farm all his life, to which old Willum replied "No, not yetawhile."

Willum was the eldest of three, the other two being Dan'll and Kate – in that order. Willum, of course, being the eldest, is head of the family now that Mum and Dad have moved on to greener pastures. Good Farmer is Willum, his father had taught him well in all aspects of husbandry. Not the fastest of workers you understand, but methodical and very thorough in all he does. Never flustered, never hurried, he's kept to just the one speed throughout his life – sotchelling, which means when translated into layman's terms – well, you know! – sotchelling! Some folks go fast, and some folks go slow, but old Willum – he just sotchells.

Dan'll, the next in line, is different. It's a job to put your finger on just how different really, but he's a bit – well, he's a bit odd. For a start, he can never quite understand why his sister has two brothers, while he only has the one, and if Willum sets him at work in the fields, then forgets to go and fetch him home at teatime, it just doesn't occur to him that perhaps he ought to walk back to the farmhouse – no, he just stays there like, ar, all blessed night if they were to leave him – and he'd still be working. Dan'll's – well, he's unable to grasp any situation really – and at the same time, a bit slow on the uptake. Dan'll's *that* sort of different.

And Kate? Well, she's altogether different from her brothers, of course, for all the right womenly reasons – ar, most of them usually quite visible. Yees, very comely is Kate – well, she was in her younger days. Flighty? Oh yes, but all the same for that, very comely. Rather in the same category as old Miss Peacock when she was younger – sowed acres of wild oats, but never quite come to terms on how to gather in the harvest. Getting a bit long in the tooth now, of course, if she's got any of her own left that is . . .

Nothing very exciting ever happens at Church Farm, except on odd occasions, like when the great barn caught fire, and Willum had to call out the Buckland Common Bucket Brigade. Then there was the time when Freddie Maynard, the Water Bailiff, walked into Church Farm dewpond, and disappeared right up to his neck in frog spawn and Jenny Green Teeth, just because he wouldn't listen to Old Willum's sound advice.

No, excitement was never very high on Willum's agenda at Church Farm, but all that changed one cold Winter's day – just before Christmas it was, when Abel Burchett with his convoy of threshing machinery pulled into Willum's rick-yard, and his team of itinerant threshers took up residence in Willums's Great Barn for the duration, which was to last up until Christmas.

Meanwhile, preparations were well in hand for the ever popular Christmas

Produce Fair that takes place annually on the Common. Holding pens had been erected and several small tents were already up and running, housing organised bodies of importance, namely the tea tent, and the toilet tent – both establishments of course essential, and entirely dependant on each other to 'make a living' – so to speak.

Even to this very day, the Annual Christmas Produce Fair attracts folks from miles around, and in bygone years it was regarded as being the top event of the year. Folks descended on the Village Common in their droves, each and every one looking for a bargain amongst the poultry pens and Christmas produce stalls, whilst inbetween times, enjoying the added attraction of the traditional Hunt meeting at the Full Moon. As always at this event, a hot chestnut seller had set up for business beside the frozen village pond, and was already doing a roaring trade.

Down at the vicarage, Brusher Morley was in deep conversation with the vicar, who was shaking his head in agitated frustration, as they discussed the finances of the Vicar's fund for the forthcoming Old Folks' Christmas Party.

"So what do you suggest we do then, Vicar?" asked Brusher, a'rattling the Christmas Fund Collection Box. "We ain't going to get very fat with just fivepence ha'penny are we?"

"You've heard the story of the Ten Wise Virgins haven't you Morley?" replied the Vicar.

"I hope they were wiser than the half a dozen we took on the charabanc trip to the seaside that time," answered Brusher.

"Oh?" queried the Vicar, "why's that then?"

"Why?" said Brusher, "because be the time we got back 'ere, Horace the Wood Turner 'ad whittled 'em down to just three."

"No, no!" the Vicar exclaimed, "the Ten Wise Virgins in the parable who had prepared their . . ."

"So 'ad the ones in the charabanc," interrupted Brusher, "but they ain't reckoned on old Horace being there."

"We'll forget the story of the Ten Wise Virgins for now," said the Vicar rather hurriedly, "and go on to . . ."

". . . Old Horace ain't never forget 'em," interruped Brusher again, "he reckons as how that wus the bestest charabanc trip we . . ."

". . . the story of the talents," carried on the Vicar, completely ignoring Brusher and his ramblings. "This is the parable where a wealthy man gives each of his three servants a certain sum of money, and instructs them to invest it wisely, thereby adding considerable interest. Now, if I were to give you our 'fivepence ha'penny talent' – how would you go about doing the same?"

"For a start, Vicar," said Brusher, "I'd go about it the opposite way to you. I would add a little to it first, then I'd invest."

"That sounds rather intriguing, Morley," exclaimed the Vicar, "so just how much would you be prepared to add, and where would you invest to gain the maximum interest?"

"That's easy," Brusher replied. "I'd add a ha'penny to it, then invest it in a couple of pints of Old and Mild down at the Rose and Crown. Now that's what I calls extremely interesting."

"Now listen, Morley," said the Vicar sternly, "this is a very serious business. It's time for action. Here we are with the Old Folks' Christmas Party just a few days away, and all we've got is fivepence ha'penny in the kitty. We've just got to raise some extra money from somewhere. Fivepence ha'penny won't buy us a turkey or a Christmas pudding and mince pies, now will it? We've got a mountain to climb, Morley, whatever are we going to do – oh dear, oh dear, whatever are we going to do?"

"Whatever are we going to do?" cried Brusher. "I'll tell you what we're going to do. Remember that time when we needed some manure for the Vicarage garden, an' you said to me . . . if we just have a little bit of faith Morley, then the good Lord will provide" . . . and suddenly, 'alf a load appeared outside the Vicarage gate? Well, he's done it once, so he can jolly well do it agin – I'm going to take the 'fivepence ha'penny talent', and we're both going to have a little bit of faith! Don't you worry Vicar, I shan't let you down – we shall get there, you'll see!"

With that, plus the Vicar's fivepence ha'penny jingling in his pocket, he picked up his wheelbarrow and made his way out of the Vicarage gates, and journeyed towards the Common . . .

The Hunt was gathering outside the Full Moon, with its numbers increasing by the minute. One of the biggest Hunts of the year this one. Everybody who was anybody at all, just had to be seen to be there. Huntsmen, and their ladies, resplendent in their colourful apparel, boots – boned to perfection, sporting such a shine, you could see your face in them – horses' nostrils expelling volumes of vapour as their warm breath condensed in the crisp air of the outside world on this bright December morning – bands of loyal Hunt followers buffeting arms and stamping feet, encouraging warmth to chilled limbs as they stood in excited groups, eagerly discussing the prospects of the day's sport – hounds sniffing around everywhere – and everybody just a'waiting for the 'off' . . .

A unique and splendid sight it has to be said, whether you're into Fox Hunting or nay.

"Righto lads!" shouted old Willum, trying frantically to make himself heard above the 'chugg chugg chugg' of the Field Marshal tractor as it gently rocked back and forth under the strain of driving the multitude of threshing machinery. Abel Burchett and his itinerant band of threshers stood standing with pitchforks raised, knives sharpened, binding wire and oil-cans poised at the ready, waiting for Willum's signal . . .

"Righto lads!" bawled Willum again, waving his arms repeatedly above his head, trying to attract some sort of attention with his own particular brand of semaphore. "Let battle commence!" and, as if by clockwork, everyone sprang into action, as the first sheaf of corn found itself on the end of a well-rehearsed pitchfork, to be thrown from the rick-top down to the thresher below, where the waiting knifeman cut the twine that bound the long stems of corn together, and spread them into the bowels of the machine.

Threshing at Church Farm was well and truly under way.

Brusher, with fivepence ha'penny of the Vicar's Christmas Party Fund, together with his own last ha'penny, rapidly burning a hole in his pocket, trundled his wheelbarrow along the road that leads to the Common. He thought perhaps he might have a look around the Christmas Produce Fair – via the Full Moon of course. As he approached the Common, the baying of the hounds, and the cheers of the Hunt followers broke into a crescendo, as the shrill blast of the hunting horn echoed across the valley, and the whole entourage began to move off across the Common, eventually to pass through the woodland that skirts the further most boundary of the cricket ground, where the hounds picked up the scent of their quarry along Hawridge Vale.

He stood and watched them until they disappeared from view, then parked his barrow outside the Full Moon, and made to enter the door, when suddenly he stopped – just like that there – turned on his heels, picked up his barrow, and made off across the Common!

What made him forsake a couple of pints on the strength of a whim we shall never know. Whether it was a slight prick of the conscience because fivepence ha'penny of the sixpence in his pocket wasn't his – although it would never have bothered him before, he'd got more than enough at home to cover it four or five times over – or whether it was the thought of the Old Folks' Christmas Party hanging in the balance, that was weighing heavily upon his shoulders. After all, the Vicar had entrusted to him, Brusher Morley, the entire contents of the Christmas Collection Box. It was entirely down to him to turn his 'fivepence ha'penny talent' into a decent Christmas treat for all the old folk.

Whatever the explanation – and for the life of him, he couldn't think of one – his mind was now fully focused on the task before him. With the Vicar's words – 'we have a mountain to climb Morley' – still ringing in his ears, he wheeled his barrow across the Common, moving in the general direction of Church Farm.

Abel's team of threshers were doing exceedingly well. The first rick was very nearly down to the bottom two or three feet – what we calls 'the interesting bit'. This part of any rick is usually home to a multitude of vermin, rats mainly, and this one was no exception. You can forget your fox-hunting – rat catching with first class terriers was, and still is, a positively humane and highly efficient way of dealing with *real* vermin, and threshing teams throughout the area considered it great sport into the bargain.

The three feet high wire netting used to encircle the rick base acting as a barricade against any vermin trying to escape, was already in place, whilst Billy Puddick the Sexton and Harry Feathers the Dung Carter, had their five terriers on 'Red Alert'.

Wagers were made between the itinerants, as to which dog would score most kills, yorks* were checked for security – don't want a rat up your trouser leg do you, could be quite painful that y'know – and makeshift cudgels grasped for walloping intending escapees via 'the over the top route'.

Excitement was now reaching feverpitch – everyone was at the ready, everyone that is, with the exception of Willum and his siblings. As the first rick was getting down to the last noggins, the next lot to be threshed was on a horse-drawn wagon loaded to capacity, a wagon which Willum was negotiating with considerable difficulty towards the threshing machine.

**Yorks*. String tied round trouser leg just below the knee as preventative against mice/rats running up inside of trousers.

Dan'll was sat on the shafts scratching his head, wondering how he was going to get off to join in the rat catching. Someone had told him he'd better get his yorks on, but he'd only got one bit of binder twine, so he tied both his legs together. It just didn't occur to him to cut the twine in half.

Kate was on top of the load, along with one of the itinerants, in order to get a better view of the rat catching – or so they explained afterwards.

Brusher found himself jostling with crowds of folks amongst the stalls at the Christmas Produce Fair. He wandered aimlessly along with his barrow, and was just wondering to himself as to why he'd come this way when he knew perfectly well that he couldn't afford to buy anything, when suddenly he stopped – just like that there – in exactly the same manner as before when he stopped in the doorway of the Full Moon. Just as he couldn't explain it then, he couldn't explain it this time either.

He looked around at the stalls, all laden with mouth-watering seasonal produce: iced cakes, mince pies, plum puddings, trifles, jellies, and trussed turkeys, geese and chickens – and a couple of tough old birds peering over the top of the Temperence Club stall – none other than Miss Peacock and old Mother Poulton.

"Now then Morley" bellowed Miss Peacock "get that old wheelbarrow out the way – there ain't nothing here that you can afford."

But on this occasion, Brusher didn't rise to the bait. His gaze was elsewhere, transfixed onto a poster he had seen many times in the past during the Great War years, when he was just a lad. It was pinned to a placard – y'know, like the ones they carry at protest meetings these days – leaning against an old post at the back of Miss Peacock.

He couldn't take his eyes off it. Although he'd seen dozens of them before – they were pinned on notice-boards throughout the country during those terrible years – this particular one seemed, well, it seemed different somehow. The war was over and done with long ago of course, but none-the-less, it seemed to Brusher that this particular poster was somehow trying to convey some sort of a message to him.

"It's trying to tell me summat," thought Brusher, "I know it is – and it's summat important like . . . like . . . life or death."

He knew at that precise moment, he must have it!

"How much d'you want for that old placard behind you?" he asked.

"This one?" queried old Miss Peacock, reaching for it.

"What d'you mean – this one," replied Brusher, "of course that one – it's the only beggar you've got."

"Is it?" she said sweetly, "that makes it more expensive then."

"How expensive?" asked Brusher, with an air of resignation about him, because he knew only too well from past experience, that she'd get every last ha'penny she could squeeze out of him, so as to prevent him from 'squandering' it all down at the Full Moon.

" 'ere we go," he said under his breath, "how much 'ave yer got in yer pockets?"

"How much have you got in your pockets?" barked Miss Peacock.

. . . "enough for a couple of pints," he said to himself.

"Enough for a couple of pints?"

. . . "Let me see," under his breath again "a couple of pints? – that'll be sixpence you've got then."

"Let me see," she mused, "a couple of pints? – that'll be sixpence you've got then."

"That's right," said Brusher out loud, resigning himself to the fact that it wouldn't be resident in his pocket for very much longer. "Sixpence, that's all I got, and fivepence ha'penny of that ain't . . ."

"That'll do," Miss Peacock bellowed, "that's far better in our pocket than it is in yourn."

So money and goods were exchanged for better or worse.

Brusher laid the purchase in his barrow and, after casting longing eyes over all that scrumptious produce, wistfully thinking to himself how nice it would look on the tables at the Old Folks Party, made off again through the jostling throng, in the direction of Church Farm, wondering whatever possessed him to buy a picture of Lord Kitchener pinned onto a placard.

He looked at it lying in his barrow. The eyes – the staring eyes – they were staring at him! The finger – the pointing finger – it was pointing at him! *Your Country Needs You* it said – and it was saying it to him! A shiver went down his spine . . . "What does it mean?" he said out loud to himself as he trudged along "what does it all mean . . . ? "

The Winter sun, half hidden behind the coppice that skirts the far side of the Common, failed to disturb the rimey hoar frost that clung to the valley floor below. The Hunt gathered momentum behind the hounds as they approached the narrow strip of scrub at the entrance to the valley, galloping on past the beech wood and into the heart of the country. Horses strung out across the blanket of white frost, taking fences in their stride, as they passed along the narrow strip of land that separated steep banks on either side, overgrown with the tall frost covered skeletons of Teasel and Rose Bay Willow Herb, which led them in turn across open stubble fields in pursuit of their quarry.

"There he goes!" was the cry, as the fox was sighted in the distance, silhouetted against the clear sky. 'Tally-hoes' abounded, competing against the rallying call of several lusty blasts on the hunting horn, and off they went again, careering along the woodland edge, hell-bent on completing the task ahead of them.

But the fox had different ideas – he was no fool this one. He'd seen a good many frosty mornings, and he was going to see a good many more. Been involved in a fair number of Hunts too, and this one was no different from the rest – same huntsmen, same horses, same hounds. He'd outrun 'em before, outfoxed 'em before, and he was about to do the same all over again. He'd done his homework well, having already done the rounds, seen what was going on up at Church Farm, watched from a safe distance as the Hunt gathered outside the Full Moon. He knew exactly what was happening – and exactly what he was going to do. His thoughts returned to the job in hand. No breakfast for him or his vixen yetawhile – there was a pressing engagement to fulfil first, and it couldn't wait a moment longer – the time was fast approaching. He was tiring now, the hounds were gaining ground, but Church Farm lay just round the next headland. He could hear the hum of the threshing machine, the 'chugg chugg chugg' of the Field Marshal . . .

His timing was nigh on perfect . . .

The fully-laden horse-drawn wagon was finally in place alongside the threshing machine. Willum was clambering up the front end on his way to the top, whilst Dan'll was still trying to figure out how to get off the shafts with both legs tied together. Kate was otherwise engaged on the top, doing what she did best . . .

On the other side of the machine, several more sheaves were hoisted aloft into the thresher from the dwindling rick base. The five terriers were unleashed and dived into the straw just as the first rat made its dash for freedom, followed by another, then two more, then another, and another. In no time at all, they were everywhere, bouncing off the wire netting barricade that encircled the rick. Terriers were after them, dashing this way, jumping that way, snarling, snapping, grabbing, biting – rats scurrying, squealing, squirming, leaping – cudgels rising and falling, swiftly dealing with those that made it to the top of the wire. Itinerants shouting, jumping up and down waving their arms in excitement, urging on their wagered favourites, bawling out instructions at the tops of their voices: "there's one! – yees – got 'im! – over there! over here! – quick, he's gettin' away – come on you good for nothin' useless beggar . . . move yerself . . . !"

Still more and more sheaves were tossed on high, feeding the insatiable appetite of the thresher, more rats running for dear life – the excitement and noise was now quite frantic – when suddenly, and without warning, all hell was let loose as the fox, right on cue, ran into the rick-yard, leaped over the wire barricade, stood there for a few seconds then jumped out over the other side, just as the hounds, closely followed by the huntsmen and their followers, came hurtling into the yard and ran full tilt into the wire netting encirclement.

The entire rick-yard was immediately plunged into a scene of complete and utter chaos – terriers chasing after scuttling rats making a do-or-die break for freedom, taking full advantage of their unexpected escape route; hounds piling on top of each other, in the ill-conceived belief that somewhere at the bottom of the pile lay their quarry, and looking for all the world more like a rugby scrum than an orderly hunting pack; huntsmen and followers milling around the yard, trampling the remaining sheaves of the rick base to shreds, at the same time shouting, hollering and generally berating the unfortunate itinerant threshing team, bawling at 'em to 'get out of the blasted way' – never minding that their preposterous intrusion into Willum's rick-yard had turned the harmony of a day's work into total disarray, and completely ruined their sport into the bargain; whilst the whipper-in, struggling desperately to separate his hounds from the writhing heap confronting him, tried in vain to make himself heard above the almighty din that emanated from such a dreadful kerfuffle.

Betsy stood patiently in the shafts of the fully laden wagon, quietly munching her way through a wedge of clover hay. Gentle old soul was Betsy, wouldn't hurt anybody or anything, but if there was one thing she couldn't abide at any price, then it was rats. She hated 'em – frightened her near to death. From where she was standing on the other side of the thresher away from the rick, she couldn't see the rat-catching going on, contained, as it were, within the confines of the wire netting encirclement. But the minute that barricade was breached she was unprotected, and when three great rats scuttled between her legs, with a snapping terrier hard on their heels, that was it! She reared up, then – with a couple of snorts and a high pitched whinney – made off down the track with the wagon trundling behind her, gaining momentum with every step. Out of the rick-yard she went, and before anybody

realised what was happening, she was off at a steady gallop down the lane, heading towards the Common.

Willum, caught halfway between top and bottom of the load as he was clambering to the top, was now hanging on for dear life, whilst Dan'll, bless him, tried to grab a'hold of the reins, but found he couldn't move, on account as when he'd tied both his legs together, he'd put the twine round the shaft as well. At least he wouldn't fall off.

At this point, Kate and the itinerant on top of the load, were completely oblivious as to what was going on . . .

Shuffling through crowds of folks at the Produce Fair with his barrow, Brusher Morley was going through the events of the morning in his mind. All he'd got for his efforts was a placard bearing a picture of Lord Kitchener pointing at him from the confines of his barrow, and an empty pocket, cruelly robbed by Miss Peacock and old Mother Poulton of the sixpence it once contained, all of it, except for his own last ha'penny, being the entire contents of the Vicar's Christmas Party Fund for the Old Folks.

"So much for me 'fivepence ha'penny talent'," he thought to himself, "I hope the old Vicar's down on his knees – that's going to need a miracle to save the Old Folks' Party this year."

Making his way towards the lane leading to Church Farm, with the Produce Fair just behind him, he was aware of shouting in the distance that seemed to be coming towards him. He didn't take too much notice of it, except to think that it was probably the Hunt, or perhaps a few stragglers that had lost track of the main body. It happened quite often after all. But as it got louder and louder, and he could hear the cries and shouting more clearly, he realised that it wasn't the Hunt or stragglers, but someone in some kind of trouble. He glanced up towards the lane, and saw, to his horror, a mobile corn rick bearing down on him – not only on him for goodness sake – but also on hundreds of folks at the Produce Fair! They were all in the direct path of Willum's runaway fully-loaded wagon. A full-scale disaster was only seconds away.

Willum, still hanging on for dear life, was shouting at the top of his voice "*Help,*

help! – a barrel of beer for anyone who can stop us – *help, help*!"

Dan'll, for the first time in his life, decided he'd better do something to help himself – so he joined in the chorus along with Willum!

. . . Kate and the itinerant were still in a world of their own, snugged down on the top of the pile doing what comes naturally . . . !

"Good grief!" hollered Brusher, "that's old Betsy, Betsy Trottwood – an' that's Willum and Dan'll a'hangin' on there! There'll be carnage if I don't do summat a bit quick!"

Without even thinking, he grabbed the first thing closest to hand – which just happened to be the placard bearing the picture of Lord Kitchener, and, with complete disregard for his own safety, stood valiantly in the pathway of the rapidly approaching runaway wagon, holding the placard in front of him shouting and a'hollering for all he was worth.

. . . "Whoa Betsy, whoa, whoa there . . . steady up do!"

Now Betsy Trottwood had heard all about Lord Kitchener, indeed, she was old enough to remember the pictures of him pinned up all over the place during the dark years of the Great War, calling young men the length and breadth of the country to go to war against a foreign foe. She also remembered with sadness, how her old Dad had the tally* tied in his tail, eventually to be called up himself to serve King and Country.

. . . But when she saw Kitchener's picture and read the words . . . *Your Country Needs You* . . . she remembered only too well, because she never saw him again.

Yes . . . she remembered well enough . . .

Whether it was these thoughts going through old Betsy's mind, and she didn't fancy joining Lord Kitchener's Army on no account because of what happened to her old Dad, or whether it was the sight of the gallant Brusher Morley standing defiantly in her way, there is no way of telling, but at the very last moment – with poor old Brusher shaking in his boots, and beginning to wish he had spent the Vicar's fivepence ha'penny on a couple of pints, instead of Lord Kitchener's portrait – Betsy Trottwood veered away from the path she was following, and made towards the frozen pond finally coming to a gentle halt next to the Hot Chestnut Stall.

Now, if there was one thing old Betsy liked more than anything – it was hot Chestnuts!

Not what you might call a regular churchgoer was Brusher, but whether it was because his legs felt like jelly, or whether it was because he just felt the need, he

* *Tally*. Ribbon tied in the tails of horses requisitioned by the Government for active service during the 1914-18 war.

wouldn't say, but still clutching the placard with the picture of Lord Kitchener pinned to it, he fell to his knees. . .

An eerie calm had descended across the length and breadth of the Common. Where once had been laughter and shouts of delight from skaters and onlookers on and around the village pond, there was now silence.

Where once had been the raucous voice of the auctioneer in the livestock pens, the noisy bartering of the bargain hunters around the Christmas stalls, coupled with the general hub-bub and chatter of several hundred folks enjoying the Christmas spirit at the biggest event in the Village Calendar, there was now silence.

All of them had been witness to the outstanding bravery of one man – with a little help from Lord Kitchener – who had averted imminent danger, and no doubt serious injury to many, and at the same time, saved the day for the Christmas Produce Fair.

Someone rushed across to Brusher, and helped him to his feet. He was aware of someone clapping, then one or two more joined in, and suddenly, the whole place erupted into a tumultuous crescendo of cheering and clapping, the likes of which you have never heard in all your born days!

He was carried shoulder high into the midst of the cheering throng, to receive the accolade of a true hero – and to show their appreciation and heartfelt gratitude for his outstanding bravery, coins and Bradbury notes* were thrown into his barrer, along with every conceivable item of produce you could think of.

There was that much stuff, they had to get Charley Buckley from the Windmill to come across with his pony and trap and cart it all away.

Even old Miss Peacock – as mean as she was – gave him a whole crateful of Best Temperance Bitter for saving their club stall, plus his sixpence back with half-a-crown interest. She offered him a kiss as well, but Brusher turned it down gracefully, which only goes to prove that there are limits to a hero's bravery.

As for old Willum, he didn't know whether to laugh or cry. His day's work up at Church Farm had come to an abrupt end, his team of itinerant threshers had lost half a day's pay, and all their wagers on the rat-catching would have to be frozen 'til tomorrow. On the other hand, things could have been much worse. If it hadn't been for Brusher Morley and Lord Kitchener, he would more'n likely have lost Betsy Trottwood, plus a wagon load of threshing corn.

On a happier note, Willum felt that the experience had done Dan'll a power of good. For the first time in his life, the idea occurred to him that perhaps he ought

*_Bradbury notes_. First paper currency to be issued following on from Gold Sovereigns during the reign of King George V. Affectionately known as 'Bradbury's' after the first signatory – John Bradbury.

to walk home, instead of waiting for someone else to take him. It's amazing what a little bit of frightening will do. Willum thought perhaps it might have had summat to do with him wanting to change his trousers . . .

On the top of the load, Kate and the itinerant quickly deciding that discretion was the better part of valour, kept their heads down. But nothing much escapes Willum's notice – he was grateful for their decision which saved his family name from acute embarrassment in front of thousands of folks – so he told them to stay there and enjoy the journey back to Church Farm . . . !

. . . which is more than can be said for the Hunt. After they had disentangled themselves, their hounds, and everything else from the wire netting encirclement, and encountered the understandable wrath of Abel Burchett and his itinerants, they conceded that the fox had won this particular encounter, so they all went home.

But give the Master of the Hunt his due. He realised that it was his responsibility to put things right at Church Farm Not only were Willum and his itinerants generously compensated for loss of earnings, damage, and disruption to a major sporting event – namely rat-catching – he also donated two gold sovereigns to the wagers' kitty, and when he heard how Brusher Morley had saved the day down on the Common, he arranged a reward for him too, in the shape of a pint of Old and Mild every day for a year, at the pub of his choice.

At the end of the day, it was a jubilant Brusher who pushed his vastly overloaded barrow along the road, lined on both sides with hundreds of folks cheering and clapping him every step of the way, followed by Charley Buckley with his equally vastly overloaded pony and trap towards the vicarage, and he knew then that his newly found fame had preceded him, for as he walked through the gates, decked with bunting that hadn't seen the light of day since the Great War of 1914-18 fluttering in the chill wind, the village band struck up with 'Onward Christian Soldiers'. They were going to play 'See the Conquering Hero Comes', but they couldn't find the music at such short notice.

Everybody, but everybody was there, and in front of them all stood the Vicar, arms outstretched, waiting to welcome home his very own personal hero, for he and he alone with the bravest of deeds had become the Saviour of the Old Folks' Christmas Party, and he was so proud of him.

He took Brusher in his arms and hugged him, then, with tears in his eyes, as he recalled the words he'd said earlier on in the day, he whispered,

"You've climbed our mountain today Morley."

"I have," said Brusher "and look what I've come down with."

That year's Christmas Party for the Old Folks was unprecedented in all the years before or since. There was that much stuff – the likes of which most of them hadn't ever seen before – that all the old folks from every village for miles around were invited, and what a party they had.

With all the money that folks threw into his barrow, it was suggested that there ought to be a lasting tribute placed somewhere to commemorate Brusher's bravery, so it was decided on a show of hands, to erect a posthumus stained glass window in the church, for future generations of villagers to admire.

"A posthumus stained glass window," says Brusher, "my word, I shall look forward to seeing that!"

It was unanimously decided that Brusher should receive the remainder of the money, after expenses, and he was duly presented with five gold sovereigns, Miss Peacock's half-a-crown, and his own original ha'penny.

As for the expenses, which, of course, was the Vicar's proverbial 'fivepence ha'penny talent', that was duly returned to the church collection box as a start for next year's party.

However, the highlight of the evening was the presentation to Brusher – by no less a person than the Lord Lieutenant himself – with the King's Bravery Medal and Citation.

BRUSHER MORLEY KBM

He's got that nailed on his wheelbarrow . . .

. . . Whilst at church on the Sunday after, the Vicar, in front of a packed congregation, gave a specially written sermon, in which he likened Brusher's deed to the story of David and Goliath; how David, against overwhelming odds – face to face with a most fearsome adversary – knocked seven bells out of old Goliath using just a sling and pebble.

"But he couldn't have achieved it," said the old Vicar wagging his finger, "without a little help from the Lord."

"Blimey!" shouted Billy Puddick from the back of the church, "old Kitchener got about a bit didn't he!"

But before that, very early on Christmas morning, after talking with Willum about the happenings in the rickyard, Brusher set off once again with his barrow, and made his way to the wood overlooking Church Farm, pausing on the way to give Betsy Trottwood a generous supply of carrots. On his arrival at the wood, he placed several objects on the ground, and retired to a spot some two hundred yards away, and sat down in his barrow – and waited.

He didn't have very long to wait. Just as the sun was rising over Church Farm on that wonderful Christmas morning, the old fox, who caused all the furore that day, came out from the depths of the wood. He edged cautiously towards the spot where Brusher had placed his objects, then quickly darted forward to pick up the

most succulent of geese, and disappeared back into the wood, reappearing a few moments later with his vixen, to pick up two of the bestest chickens you ever did see.

All that remained of Brusher's objects was the placard of Lord Kitchener pointing at the fox as he walked back into the wood with his reward . . .

YOUR COUNTRY NEEDS YOU

it said . . . and underneath it, Brusher had written . . .

SO DID WE

He picked up his barrow, and started off back to the village, just pausing to glance back over his shoulder.

"Happy Christmas old son," he said, "and thank you." He turned, and walked back home.

Ah, the Lord certainly does move in mysterious ways, his wonders to perform . . .

. . . I do believe a substantial pinch of salt is required the next time I visit the Tap Room!

~ 5 ~
The Buckland Common Bucket Brigade

LET ME SEE – what was it going to be tonight? Samuel Mortlock's Fire Brigade, or Charley Buckley's Dawdling Bug? What's that you say – both of them? Well now, let's see how the time goes shall we?

Now then, you see that old red rounded-bottomed fire bucket a'hanging up over there by the window? Well, I won that off Charley Buckley y'know, years ago – and my word, that's seen some action has that old bucket.

I mind the very day I won that! I was pushing me barrer past the Windmill at the time, the Friday before Harvest Festival up at the church – 1935 it were. I remember that on account as that was the year of the biggest and bestest funeral Buckland Common had ever seen – but more of that later. As I was saying, I was just pushing me barrer past Charley Buckley's Windmill, when he comed out through the gate.

"I say Brusher," he says, "d'you want to buy an old fire bucket?"

"A fire bucket?" I says, "what do I want with an old fire bucket?"

"Well," he says, "that's got a nice round solid bottom."

"Yes," I says, "so's old Miss Peacock – and I don't want her neither!"

"You can have it for half-a-crown," says Charley.

"What?" I says, "half-a-crown? That's a bit hot for a fire bucket ain't it?"

"A bit hot?" says Charley, "well! – if you can show me something round here what's got a bottom as solid as that, and a mouth that's half as big, what ain't worth more that half-a-crown – why, why then I'll give it to you!"

Well, d'you know, them words ain't hardly left his lips, when who should come along but old Miss Peacock. Well, I looked at her – and then at old Charley – and he just give me the bucket!

He wanted to sell me some wire netting as well, y'know, but I weren't having none of that – not to start with anyway. Hooor, that was some rare stuff that was. Well, that was cram-packed full of holes! Ha! I ain't as daft as I look y'know! But when he said he would only charge me for the wire, and I could have the holes for nothing! Well! You don't turn away a bargain now, do you!

Ar, that's been a handy old bucket over the years y'know, but none more so than the very next day, when I filled it up with taters from orf me allotment, and took them up to church for the Harvest Festival.

They wus all up there y'know: Miss Peacock, Mrs Turvey, old Mother Poulton – and the rest of them – getting things ready for the Sunday morning service.

I wus just a'going in through the porch, when Miss Peacock stopped me.

"Ha!" she says, a'looking into me bucket, and raising her voice so's everybody else could hear, "your taters ain't very big, are they!"

So I says "No Miss," I says, "I growed them to fit my mouth – not yourn!" Ha! – that had her!

Just then, Billy Puddick the Sexton comed in, carrying a bucketful of flowers.

"Hello," says Miss Peacock poking her nose into Billy's bucket, "they're nice ain't they – Sweet Williams and Sweet Pea?"

"No," says Billy, "Sweet Williams and water!"

Well, well, that done it!

"Ooooh!" she says, "you're disgusting. Just for that I'll have some of them to take home," and went to grab a bunch from out of the bucket. That's the same every year! She does that every Harvest Festival y'know – but this time Billy had come prepared, and as she put her hand into the bucket, there was one h'almighty snap – y'know, just like elastic busting!

Well, you never see'd nothing like it! Mrs Turvey and old Mother Poulton both made a grab for their drawers – only that weren't them at all! But you should have heard Miss Peacock! She was a'hollering fit to bust! She clarred her hand out of the bucket, and there, clinging to the end of her fingers, was one of Billy's mouse traps.

"Gotcha!" says Billy.

"Oh dear, oh dear!" I says, "now what are you going to do?"

"I don't know," he says, "when I catches them at home, I either chucks them over the hedge – or gives them to the cat."

"Well," I says, "you ain't never caught one as big as that before."

"You're right!" says Billy, "I shall want a bit of help to chuck her over the hedge!"

In the end, seeing as how she weren't quite dead, Billy let her go. He's like that y'know – kindhearted really. Poor old Miss Peacock, I bet that didn't half tingle.

"Oooooh!" she says, "oooooh!" a'wringing her fingers and prancing up and down the aisle. "Fancy bringing that to Harvest Festival – that ain't a flower."

"Oh, I dunno," says Billy, "how about a Snapdragon."

Y'know, I reckon Billy's buckets are just like Miss Peacock's drawers – that ain't worth your while trying to pinch what's inside, but if you do try – then keep your hands well away from the bottom!

They got me to join the Fire Brigade y'know, on account as I got me own bucket. Samuel Mortlock wus the Fire Chief, which wus only fair really, seeing as how we used his hearse as the fire engine – when it wus empty!

There wus five of us in the Brigade y'know, which wus handy really, because Sam's old hearse held us all just nicely – four sitting down and one laying. I mind I felt quite privileged when I first joined y'know. Well, most folks only reckon to get one ride in a hearse don't they!

I mind the first ride I ever had in that old hearse. Seeing as how I wus new to the job, I wus the one that had to lay down of course.

"Dear me!" I says, as we wus a'bowling along the road, "ain't that beggar bumpy. I reckon I can feel every one!"

"You make the most of them then," says old Sam, "because there'll come a day when you won't feel any of them at all!"

Sam's horse, old Strawberry, used to pull the village charabanc at one time y'know, and old habits die hard with horses, just as they do with us folkses sometimes. I mind we wus a'going along the road in the hearse one time, when old Strawberry forgot herself and pulled up at the bus stop. 'Course, old Sam wus a bit of a wag y'know, and quick as a flash he hollered out "We've got room for one inside!" Well, you ought to have seen them folkses at the bus stop move! They wus all there one minute, and all gorn the next.

"Well Sam," I says, "you ain't got one taker."

"Never mind," he says, "I expect there'll come a day when I shall take all of 'em – eventually!"

'Course, the Fire Brigade ain't like it used to be years ago, when we had to dip our buckets in the pond to fill 'em up. That's easy now of course, 'cos the water comes in pipes. You just fixes the hoses to the fire hydrant, and squirts the water straight into your bucket! Saves a lot of time that does!

Freddie Maynard wus the Water Bailiff in them days. He used to walk when he first started coming round y'know – 'til he got his-self a bike. An old Raleigh it were. Everybody called him Walter after that – can't think why. But I like Freddie best. Well, Walter Maynard don't sound quite right really does it?

Ha, I mind when he first had that old bike. That wus the same day he'd asked old Sam where the village pond wus, you know the one I mean don't you – the same one that me and old Billy fell into in our Gel Guide uniforms! Anyway, old Freddie weren't used to riding a bike y'know, and he weren't too steady to start orf with, and he kept on a'falling orf. He fell into the pond a couple of times, once when we wus passing by in the hearse.

Quick as a flash Sam hollers out "Hello, I see you've found it then. Checking the depth?"

And the answer came back just as quick "No, I'm stocktaking!"

They wus always having a friendly go at each other after that y'know. I remember the time when Freddie stuck them there hydrant signs up all over the place, you know the ones, big old yeller'uns what's got an 'H' on them, and numbers top and bottom. He put them up so's he knowed where his water pipes wus.

He showed 'em to old Sam y'know.

"Well," says Sam, "whatever might they be for then?"

"I'll show you," says Freddie, taking a couple of signs out of his saddlebag, and pointing to the numbers on them.

"This one tells me that the hydrant is five foot out that way, and four foot deep. This one," he says, "tells me that the water pressure is 100lbs to one square inch."

"Hmm – that ain't what that tells me," says Sam, 'cause he liked a bit of a gamble y'know.

"Oh?" says Freddie, "so what does it tell you then?"

"Why," says Sam, as he knocked his pipe ash into Freddie's saddlebag, "that one tells me that it's 4-to-5-on that your saddlebag is going to catch a'fire – and this one," he says, "tells me that it's 100-to-1-against us finding any water to put the beggar out with!" and d'you know, the very next second, Freddie's saddlebag went up in flames, along with all his sandwiches!

"Help! Help!" bellows old Freddie, still sat on his old bike. "Do something!"

"Look sharp!" shouted Sam, "pedal like hell and make for the pond." And so he did, with all us chaps a'running after him – and we catched him up just as he disappeared into the water, with a h'almighty splash and a cloud of smoke!

"Well," says Sam, as we dragged Freddie and his bike out of the pond for the third time that week, "that goes to prove one thing beyond any doubt whatsoever don't it?"

"Oh?" wailed Freddie, "whatever might that be then?"

"Why," says old Sam, "the old ways are always the best, of course. That wus a lot quicker than us trying to find your hydrant!"

Oh dear, oh dear, we've had many a laugh over that I can tell you. Poor old Freddie. But he took it all in good part y'know, and him and Sam always remained the best of pals.

But we had some good times in Samuel Mortlock's wonderful Fire Brigade. Ha, I mind one particular cold winter's morning, when Willum's old barn catched alight up at Church Farm. That lays up there just beyond the Common y'know.

Old Sam rounded us all up, and off we went at a gallop. I wus laying down as usual, but this time old Sam had put some nice clean sacks in the hearse for me to lay on – which wus good of him I thought at the time.

But before that it took Sam a good half hour to catch old Strawberry, and be the time he'd called in the Rose and Crown, the Full Moon and the White Lion a'rounding up the rest of us and had one or two his-self – well, you can't call in a pub without having a pint now can you? – by the time we got to Church Farm, that old barn fire wus going just nicely!

"That's nice and hot," says Billy Puddick, warming his hands. "Seems a shame to put it out don't it!"

"Happen you're right," says Percy Lamkin, pulling his tea bottle and some sandwiches from out of Strawberry's nose-bag. "Let's have our lunch afore we start."

Well, we'd just got ourselves sat down on our buckets, when up comed old Willum, waving his arms about and shouting at the top of his voice!

"Hello," says Billy Puddick, "he don't seem very happy. I wonder what's bothering him?"

"Oi! Oi! Oi!" shouted Willum, "what d'you lot reckon you're a'doing?"

"Doing?" says Sam, "why, having our lunch!"

"Having your lunch? Having your lunch?" he hollers, "there's you lot a'stuffing sandwiches down your gullets, while I got a cart-load of taters a'cooking in that barn!"

"That's nice," says Sam, a'looking at the fire, "give it another five minutes, and they should be done just nicely."

"Ooooh!" says Willum, "I got a load of turnips in there an' all!"

"Ah well," says Sam, "in that case, they'll want a few minutes longer then!"

But old Willum got it right in the end y'know, because when he just happened to mention that he'd got a 40 gallon barrel of Best Bitter, left over from the 'Harvest Home', what ain't even been tapped yet, a'laying in the far corner of the barn – why, you never see'd five firemen move so fast in all your born days!

'Course, that wus just the nod that old Sam had been waiting for. Well, every job's got its perks ain't it, and of course, old Willum knowed that!

I found out then what them sacks wus for, y'know, them ones what I thought old Sam had put in the hearse for me to lay on – because we formed a bucket chain from the duck pond to the barn, and for every bucket of water as went in, a bucketful of taters comed out – tipped straight into the sacks and chucked into the hearse!

We all got as black as soot from that old smoke y'know, but we had that fire out in no time at all, and, of course, we managed to salvage the barrel of beer! That had a little hole in it where that got a bit scorched, so of course we had to fill up our buckets!

But what with the hearse being filled up with taters and that, there weren't a lot of room left for us chaps, so we all sat on the top of them, and drove back through the village to Sam's place. And d'you know, to this very day, the folks up there still talk about the time when Samuel Mortlock's old hearse comed slowly through the village, piled so high with bodies that the mourners – dressed all in black from head to toe, drinking out of pots as big as – as big as fire buckets, and singing for all they wus worth at the top of their voices – had to sit on top of them to hold them all on!

They reckoned as how that wus the biggest, the bestest, and the happiest funeral as ever took place in Buckland Common – the likes of which nobody had ever seen before, nor yet since!

. . . Yes – that old rounded-bottomed fire bucket a'hanging up there holds a good many happy memories for me.

Now then, d'you reckon we've got time for this next one? After you've got me another pint in you say? Why, that's very kind of you!

Charley Buckley's Dawdling Bug weren't it? But before we start, let's have a bit more coal on that fire, shall we?

Ah, that's better . . .

Brusher Morley's story continues on page 64

~ 6 ~
Pack up your Troubles in your Old Kit Bag

JUST WHO HE WAS nobody really knew. Henry Billinge, for that was his name, used to be the '2d-a-week Packman'* for a firm out of London, dealing in all manner of merchandise. No matter what it was, or who it was for – be it farmers, parish councils, churches, or the general public – if you wanted it, he could get it.

Every two weeks regular as clockwork, would find him trudging up Hawridge Hill out of Chesham Vale, pencil behind his ear, notebook at the ready, and singing. He was always singing – hymns, anthems and canticles – and anything else he felt was necessary, because he didn't just sing for pleasure's sake, oh dearie me no, most of his singing had a definite purpose, more of an ulterior motive if you like – but more of that later.

Now you might be asking yourself "why would he need his notebook at the

**Packman.* Term first used in 1582. A man who travels about carrying goods in a pack for sale – a Pedlar

ready?" especially up Hawridge Hill, seeing as how there aren't any houses there until you get right to the top. Well, that's just where you could be wrong y'see, because you never know who might be lurking about behind a tree or a hedge, either just not wanting to see you, or desperately trying to avoid you – and there is a difference y'know. Whichever way it is, of course, is entirely dependent on whether or not they owe you money – and that's just how it was with Henry Billinge. Some didn't and some did, although it never seemed to bother him too much. He knew he'd be paid sooner or later – one way or another.

But in truth, nobody ever knew where he came from, where he lived, or how he got here – especially how he got here. He just seemed to appear – just like that there – and it was always halfway up the hill. Not at the bottom, not at the top, but always halfway. It was what you might call a bit uncanny really. He never came by car because he didn't have one – not as far as anybody knew. There weren't that many about in those days anyway, just the odd one or two, and he would never ever accept a lift from any passing transport whatever sort it was, preferring instead to walk everywhere.

He worked to the theory that if he wasn't in full control over when and where he wanted to be, he would more than likely miss out on a possible sale – and he wasn't having that.

But he rarely missed much did Henry. They do say he could see right round corners, over the top of walls, and straight through hedges – even the thickest of privet. They reckoned he had telescopic lenses in them old bottle glasses he wore. They were that powerful, they made his eyes look like organ stops. He could see through anything and anybody – until he came up to Buckland Common that is.

Top man at his job was this '2d-a-week Packman' – or so he'd have everybody believe by the way he was talking. Before he started out on the serious business of selling, he'd researched every house, every cottage, farm, pub, church and club, plus their occupants, and familiarised himself with everybody's occupation, marital status, religion and pastime, with information he had gathered from what he termed 'a very reliable source' – within the confines of the Rose and Crown.

Little did he realise that his 'very reliable source' – namely Brusher Morley – had acted with the good of the village and the safety of its villagers uppermost in his mind, and had passed on the information accordingly.

It's a pity he didn't ask his informant about village rules and etiquette before he started boasting. He would probably have saved himself a great deal of trouble if he had, but he was to find out soon enough that life's not all plain sailing – particularly if Brusher Morley had anything to do with it.

Henry now knew all there was to know about the people he had been advised to call on by his 'very reliable source', and he was going to have a field day calling on his considerable expertise and vast experience in dealing with people, in order to sell as much merchandise as he could, and make himself a few Bradburys in the process – or so he thought.

So it was a very confident Henry Billinge, taking his first intrepid steps into the vast unknown of the hilltop villages, who strode purposefully to his first port of call on Hawridge Common – a little low-eaved white painted cottage known as The Old Crabtree.

He read his notes carefully as he strode along.

"Hmm," he says to himself, "a certain Mrs Peacock lives here: 1st Reserve Organist at the Wesleyan Reform; Chairman of Vice at the Women's Institute; Third in command of the 1st Hawridge and Cholesbury Girl Guides, and her favourite hymn is – oh ar, I know that one well enough. A very timid lady, easily frightened, needs to be handled with discretion – sounds like a nice easy one to start off with – oh yes . . . 'and knock as loud as you can' said my informant in the Rose and Crown . . . 'she's very deaf'. . . Now what on earth was his name? – Marney? No, that wasn't it – Morley? Yes, yes, that was it, Morley – Brusher Morley – silly old duffer he was – several trips to the pub Tap Room and I weedled out of him all the information I shall need – and all for the price of a few pints of Old and Mild. Some folks would sell their own grandmother for a few . . . Ah! Here we are. The Old Crabtree."

He walked briskly up the garden path, taking not a blind bit of notice of the sign on the five-barred gate that said

STRICTLY NO HAWKERS
NO CIRCULARS
AND NO PACKMEN

Then straightening his tie and adjusting his pork-pie* as he went (whilst singing in his far from melodious voice four verses of what his 'very reliable source' told him was Miss Peacock's favourite: Hymns Ancient and Modern No. 285 'Fierce rages the tempest in the deep') he proceeded to knock on the door!

Inside The Old Crabtree, Miss Peacock was half asleep with Popsy her Jack Russell sat on her lap, dreaming of the new organ they desperately needed up at the church where she was organist – when there came this almighty *rat-a-tat, rat-a-tat, rat-a-tat-tat, rat-a-tat, rat-a-tat, rat-a-tat-tat* on her front door knocker, accompanied by the most appalling rendition of her favourite most-hated hymn of all time. She shot bolt upright in the chair, arms and legs flailing everywhere, frightened near to death. Popsy was thrown violently to the floor, colliding on the way down with the small coffee table that was supporting Miss Peacock's more than adequate legs – that fell

**Pork-pie.* Hat with flat rimmed crown and brim turned up all round.

over, at the same time as did the three-parts-filled glass of sherry that had been balancing very precariously on the arm of the chair – with Miss Peacock swiftly following suit – half landing on poor old Popsy, who objected somewhat and promptly bit her finger! She rolled over to get out of range of Popsy's teeth, hollering as she went, and cut her leg on a bit of glass – being all that remained of her mid-morning glass of sherry!

In the meantime, Henry Billinge was still knocking on the door, and singing at the top of his voice, completely oblivious to the scene of mayhem and blood-letting that was occurring behind the still as yet unanswered, fiercely-knocked door . . .

Henry Billinge could tell the moment Miss Peacock flung open the door, that her intentions were anything but honourable. Clutching the door-knocker in one hand and his bagful of samples and catalogues in the other, he was unceremoniously yanked off his feet, and came to rest dumped face-down on the doormat, just as he was singing the last line '. . . lest we sink to rise no more' of Miss Peacock's favourite hymn (according to his 'very reliable source' – whose reliability was now raising an inkling of doubt in his mind).

"Do I have the pleasure of addressing Mrs Peacock?" bleated Henry, mumbling as best he could through the dirt and grime of the doormat. "1st Reserve Organist at the Wesleyan Reform, Chairman of Vice at the Women's Institute, and Third in Command of the 1st Hawridge and Cholesbury Girl Guides?" whilst at the same time grovelling for his porky-pie that had come to rest in front of him. But he wasn't quite quick enough. It wasn't too often that Popsy met up with a travelling '2d-a-week Packman' – and even less often on a level playing field so to speak. He looked Henry straight in the eye, growled a couple of times, decided he didn't like him very much and let his feelings be known, in no uncertain terms, by promptly piddling in the perimeter of his pristine porky-pie.

"Pleasure?" thundered Miss Peacock, picking Henry up by the lapels of his raincoat. "Pleasure? The only pleasure you'll get when I've finished with you, is when you walk back through the front gate" as she boxed both his ears "if you're able . . ." She suddenly stopped in full flow as she realised fully what Henry Billinge had just said . . .

"1st Reserve Organist . . . Wesleyan Reform . . . Chairman of Vi . . . ? and Third – *Third!* in command . . . ? *How dare you!*" she bellowed at the top of her voice, "I'll have you know that I'm *Head* Organist at St Mary's Church of England in Cholesbury, *Chairman* of the Hawridge-cum-Cholesbury Women's Institute, *and Chief Guider* – that's *Chief Guider!* – of the 1st Hawridge-cum-Cholesbury-cum-St Leonards-cum-Buckland Common Girl Guides . . . and what do you mean by trying to knock me door down, I'm not deaf y'know. And why are you singing that infernal hymn, I hate it, who put you up to it? You're not carol singing are you? Yes you are, you're carol singing – no you're not! – nobody goes carol singing in March! You're begging! That's what you're doing – begging – a grown man begging on the doorstep of a poor defenceless woman. You're nothing but a common beggar – take that!" and she gave him a few more cuffs round both ears for good measure.

Poor Henry Billinge. He looked like a battlefield, but, like the true '2d-a-week Packman' he was, he didn't give up. He'd never been accused of being a beggar before, and to be called one now – that really hurt! He drew himself up to his full height, which brought him eye-to-eye with Miss Peacock's ample bosoms, and uttered a phrase that has since been immortalised, and made the name of Henry Billinge* famous the world over . . .

"Madam," he said, "I travel in ladies underwear."

Well, that done it! He took one look at the steam collecting rapidly on his bottle glasses as Miss Peacock pressed her face into his, and quickly decided that discretion was the better part of valour. He legged it as fast as ever he could down the garden path, took a very apprehensive look at the five-barred gate that stood between him and freedom, decided he hadn't either the time or the inclination to stop and open it – and took off!

He did very well really. He managed to clear four bars out of the five! However, he caught his foot in the fifth, did a cartwheel over the top, and very fortuitously landed on the opposite side of the gate. His bag flew open, and several catalogues scattered themselves amongst the daffodils by the roadside. He scrabbled up, grabbed his bag, and shot off down through the wood opposite, with Popsy snapping at his heels – whilst the voice of Miss Peacock echoed like a foghorn over the valley below

. . . *"and I'm not a Mrs – I'm a Miss . . . I'm a Miss!"*

"You certainly are," Henry gasped, as he slithered down a steep bank in a successful effort to rid himself of the very persistent needle sharp teeth of Popsy. "I shall definitely give you one next time."

He sat down on a convenient tree trunk to regain his somewhat shattered composure, and reflect on his catastrophic opening call.

"I never experienced anything like this in London," he panted, "so where did I go wrong – just where did I go wrong?"

He sat silently on the tree trunk, turning the events over in his mind whilst examining the damage to his porky-pie, which was rather damp, smelt a trifle unsavoury, but otherwise unharmed, and therefore remained quite serviceable. He pulled his notes from his pocket.

"Now then Billinge," he said, "any 2d-a-week Packman worth his salt never gives

**Billinge.* Village of. (Lancs), and Billinge Beacon. Probably both named after Henry Billinge.

up – so let me see, who's the next one, ah yes, here we are – Annie Lovegrove, Buckland Common Post Office and General Store. Hmm, I'm going to completely disregard that idiot Brusher Morley's information on this particular lady – in fact, I'm not going to read it at all. It's always been my experience that persons who run post offices and general stores are most amiable towards their customers and members of the general public – so come on, put the calamitous Miss Peacock behind you, get your backside off this tree trunk *and go for it!*"

He picked up his bag of samples and the remaining catalogues, and, bursting into a rousing chorus of 'Onward Christian soldiers, marching as to war' he strode positively towards the uncharted waters of Buckland Common . . . and Annie Lovegrove.

Having finished all the verses of 'Onward Christian Soldiers', Henry Billinge had by this time accrued quite a gallery of snotty-nosed kids all following on behind . . . reminiscent of the style of the 'Pied Piper of Hamlyn' strangely attracted by his singing . . . or was it perhaps just saying amongst themselves "Come on, let's follow this silly old twirp and see where he's going" – you know what snotty-nosed kids are like. He burst into a chorus of 'My heart may be like a garden fair' with all the kids that attended Sunday School joining in with the rest of it "da da da da da da da a'blossoming there"* (kids never did remember all of the second line did they?) as he drew near to Buckland Common Post Office and General Store, with its well manicured lawn, and flower beds full of the joys of Spring.

*'With loving words and thoughts and deeds a'blossoming there.'

He threw caution to the wind, and so – to the strains of Hymns Ancient and Modern No. 540 'Fight the good fight with all thy might' from his snotty-nosed band of faithful followers, who knew a great deal more about Annie Lovegrove than he did, simply because he declined to read the notes from 'his reliable source' – he boldly approached the entrance to the shop, giving the appearance of a man who had gone some way to recovering his dignity and courage.

However, the fearsome jangling of the brass bell on the inside of the imposing shop door had a sobering effect on Henry, and he reverted to a somewhat cautious entrance into the world of Annie Lovegrove's Post Office and General Store.

"Good morning Madam!" exclaimed Henry, doffing his soggy porky-pie in the direction of an exceedingly large woman, standing with her back to him behind the shop counter "Do I have the pleas. . . "

"Get that dog out of my shop," bellowed Annie Lovegrove, without even bothering to turn round.

"Dog?" winced Henry, glancing round the shop, "Dog? What dog?"

"The one that came in with you of course," she bellowed again, still without turning round. "There ain't no other dog in 'ere is there! – can't you read? *No dogs allowed in this shop*! It says so on the door."

"I haven't got a dog!" exclaimed Henry.

Annie at last left off what she was doing, swung round, directed her gaze towards the source of the unfamiliar voice, then staggered back a pace in astonishment at the spectacle before her.

As well she might too, because from the very smartly turned out dapper little '2d-a-week Packman' who entered the village a short time ago, Henry Billinge had degenerated into something on a par with Willum Trottwood's scruffiest scarecrow. His mud spattered raincoat hung in tatters where Popsy had been hanging on the end of it, his patent leather shoes were all scuffed and caked in mud where he'd cartwheeled over the five-barred gate, his knees were poking through his trousers where he'd slid down the steep bank, and finally, his best porky-pie was still soaking wet with that smelly unmentionable liquid – courtesy of Popsy! At the same time as Annie Lovegrove's mouth dropped open, Henry Billinge just couldn't believe his eyes either, or his unbelievable bad luck. He'd just escaped from one lion's den, and here he was walking straight into another.

Annie Lovegrove was just *enormous*, with arms the size of beer-barrels, and a chest the likes of which he'd never seen before. Henry's whole life flashed before his eyes, and the words 'out of the frying pan and into the fire' repeatedly raced through his befuddled brain.

"A tramp!" she screamed at last, "you're a tramp!" She sniffed, loudly, and then sniffed again . . . "and a smelly one at that! Are you sure you ain't got a dog concealed in them filthy clothes somewhere, because that's what it smells like to me?" She ventured a little closer, sniffing loudly as she did so.

"It's that hat!" she cried, "whatever have you done to it – it smells worse than sheep dip!"

"Oh that," said Henry, backing off a little, not really wanting to see the whites of Annie's eyes, "Miss Peacock's dog cocked his leg over it."

"Pray tell me do," replied Annie sweetly, at the same time discreetly reaching for the old cricket bat that she kept handy for repelling undesirables, "just how did that little old dog manage to reach right up there and piddle on your porky-pie – from the top rung of a step ladder perhaps?"

"Oh no," said Henry, with a sense of relief at the mellowing change in Annie's tone of voice, completely unaware of the extreme peril he was being drawn into, "I was laying down on her mat at the time . . . "

Wallop, wallop, wallop! interrupted the cricket bat, as it descended upon the packman's unprotected backside with the force of two large beer-barrels! *Wallop, wallop, wallop*!

"*Do you expect me to believe that!*" yelled Annie, "what do take me for? *Get out – get out of my shop, you filthy old tramp!*" – and the cricket bat rose and fell a dozen times more as Henry Billinge felt the full force of the Buckland Common Postmistress's wrath, as she lathered his backside.

It came as a feeling of immense relief to Henry, when he was at last thrown out of Annie's shop by the scruff of the neck, closely followed by his bag of redundant samples and catalogues. His snotty-nosed little chums, who had witnessed the whole fracas from the comparitive safety of behind the shop window, gave him a hero's welcome as he came flying out through the door, closely followed by Annie Lovegrove.

Quite a crowd had gathered now, and as Annie stood over the unfortunate '2d-a-week Packman', with her six-hitting cricket bat poised ready to strike yet again, they all as one burst into a rousing chorus of Hymns Ancient and Modern No: 135 'The strife is o'er, the battle done, now is the victor's triumph won!', just to help him on his way. At that very moment, Billy Puddick the Sexton appeared along with Brusher Morley and his wheelbarrow. They loaded the exhausted Henry on board, and pushed him all the way back to the wheelbarrow park at the Rose and Crown where it all began just a few hours earlier, and unceremoniously tipped him out.

"Well, thank you too Mr Morley," said Henry, picking himself up from off the ground.

"You're welcome," said Brusher casually, as he and Billy made their way towards the saloon bar, "it's all part of the interview."

"Interview?" exclaimed Henry indignantly. "What interview? I never asked for an interview."

"Nobody asks for an interview when they comes to the Hilltop Villages," Brusher replied, "they just gets one – now come on in, it's time to meet the Selection

Committee for their decision."

"Interview? Selection Committee? Decision?" muttered Henry Billinge to himself, scratching his head as he followed Billy and Brusher through the pub door. "Whatever is going on?"

"Mr Henry Billinge," announced Brusher, in his best authoritative voice to the five distinguished looking gentlemen seated round a table in the saloon bar. "Mr Billinge," he continued "meet Mr Samuel Mortlock, Undertaker; Dr Percy Simmons, the village GP; Mr Albert Mawdesley, Parish Clerk; Major-General Rivington-Pike, retired; and the Rev. Charles Ashurst, Vicar of St Mary's, and Chairman of the Hilltop Villages Selection Committee."

"Pray sit down," said the Vicar. "Good grief Billinge," he exclaimed with a sniff "you do rather niff – have you been piddled upon?"

"Good grief Billinge," chorused the committee, half rising out of their seats, then exclaiming with a sniff, "you do rather niff – have you been piddled upon?"

"Ah! – yees," responded Mr Maudesley, the Parish Clerk, blowing a great cloud of dust all over the committee from a pile of papers in front of him, then peering over the top of his pince-nez. "That'll be Popsy, Miss Peacock's little old dog." Upon perusal of the Parish Papers Pertaining to Packmen, it would appear that – without exception – Miss Peacock's Popsy has positively piddled 'pon them all.

"Quite so Mawdesley," retorted the vicar, "quite so, but no matter – Morley, Puddick – your reports on Mr Billinge if you please."

"Well," said Brusher, "he got his-self chucked out of Miss Peacock's cottage, I see'd it all from behind a tree on the Common . . . "

". . . And he *also* got chucked out of *Annie Lovegrove's shop*" interrupted Billy Puddick, "I watched it from behind the privet hedge next door – I couldn't believe it!"

"*What?*" A mighty roar rent the air as the whole committee rose from their seats as one . . . "*What? Chucked out of Annie Lovegrove's shop? – chucked out of Annie Lovegrove's shop and Miss Peacock's cottage – all on the same day?*"

"All on the same day," repeated Brusher Morley and Billy Puddick solemnly, "all on the same day."

. . . "*And* without any retaliation," added Brusher.

. . . "*And* without any retaliation?" repeated the committee . . . "*incredible!*"

The Vicar turned to address his fellow members. "Gentlemen," he said, "I think we have heard enough. I would even go as far as to say, that what we have here is undoubtedly a unique situation. Never before, in all the years we have been meeting together to decide the fate of a '2d-a-week Packman' – and there have been many such meetings – not one of the gentlemen concerned has ever, after having his ears soundly boxed, been piddled upon, and finally chucked out of Miss Peacock's cottage, has ever had the courage to carry on! For Billinge here to have done so, is bravery far beyond the call of duty. I therefore propose a vote in the affirmative . . . "

"What does that mean?" whispered Billy.

"I think it means old Billinge 'ere has got the job," replied Brusher.

"Quite so Morley," said the Vicar, "quite so . . . all those in favour raise your hands. Just as I thought – carried unanimously, and Billinge, just a word in your ear if I may. If you want to get on the right side of Miss Peacock, she desperately needs a new organ – up at the church you understand. If you happen to come across one in your travels . . . "

"So what was that all about then, Mr Morley?" said Henry Billinge afterwards, as he sat in the Tap Room with Brusher and Billy.

"Rules and etiquette," replied Brusher. "Rules and etiquette – we can't have any old Tom, Dick, or Harry roaming around up 'ere y'know – never know who they might be. Strangers have to be vetted, tried and tested; vetted to make sure they are who they say they are, and then tried and tested to find out if they are as dedicated to the job as they make out to be. When you sat on that tree trunk after you escaped from Miss Peacock, and you decided to carry on, I knew you were dedicated alright, in spite of all your boasting and calling me an idiot. So it's well done, Mr Billinge, you've been accepted as the Hilltop Villages first ever '2d-a-week Packman'."

"But I didn't take an order," exclaimed Henry, "I didn't take one order."

"That's no problem," said Billy butting in, as he looked up from one of the catalogues he'd salvaged from amongst the daffodils outside Miss Peacock's cottage, "we can soon alter that."

"Right!" cried Henry, fetching out his notebook, "that's great – so what are you having then?"

"A double whisky," said Billy, "and a pint of Old and Mild," said Brusher.

"Cheers!"

It was a painful but happy Henry Billinge who walked down Hawridge Hill in the early evening sunshine – and much wiser than the one who ascended it earlier in the day.

On the one hand, he had been subjected to the roughest, the toughest, and the most painful interview of his entire career, but had emerged triumphant (although somewhat bedraggled and sore) at the other end!

He would return in two weeks, safe in the knowledge that he would never again have to run the gauntlet of a first interview with Miss Peacock and Annie Lovegrove. On the other hand, he realised he would inevitably have to face them both again sometime in the future – but not until his earholes had stopped ringing, and his backside had healed.

He had learned a lot in a short space of time, from people a good deal smarter than he had ever given them credit for.

He learned first and foremost that country folk are not to be messed with.

Secondly, he learned to be discreet. Never ask anybody in a pub for information concerning people in the village – others, maybe less honest than yourself, may be listening, and so the chances are you will more'n likely finish up with all the wrong answers – just as Henry did. And look at the price he paid!

And, thirdly, always look behind trees, over brick walls, and through privet hedges – you just never know who might be lurking behind them . . . now what was it the Vicar had whispered in his ear – something about Miss Peacock wanting a new organ . . . ?

. . . Maybe, just maybe there *was* a chink in Miss Peacock's armour . . . !

With that thought in mind, he slung his bag containing his not-so-redundant samples and catalogues across his shoulder, and burst into that old perennial favourite

'Pack up your troubles in your old kit-bag and
smile, smile, smile . . .'

And so it was, that Henry Billinge came to the end of his first day in what was to become a multitude of fortnightly visits to the Hilltop Villages, spanning a period of no less than forty-five years.

His ever increasing band of snotty-nosed kids grew up to produce even more snotty-nosed kids – all eager to be associated with 'Henry's Happy Band of Pilgrims'.

Henry Billinge was to become a well-loved, and much revered man – a legend in his own lifetime, and none more so than in the Sunday Schools, where the kids at 'Chorus request time' always asked – and still ask to this very day – for Henry's all time favourite . . .

'My heart may be like a garden fair –
*da da da da da da da a'blossoming there.'**

(and they *still* can't remember the second line).

As the sun disappeared, and Henry vanished into the gathering gloom halfway down the hill from whence he came, the strains of 'Pack up your troubles in your

*'My heart may be like a garden fair.' *CSSM Chorus Book No. 288.*

old kit-bag' came wafting through the still air, and his faithful band of snotty-nosed kids who had been following him about for most of the day, shouted out to their new found friend . . .

"Cheerio Henry – see you next time."

They all turned around, and then, singing the rest of the song at the top of their voices . . .

"While you've a Lucifer to light your fag,
Smile boys that's the style.
What's the use of worrying, it never was worth while,
so – pack up your troubles in your old kit-bag
and smile – smile – smile"

. . . walked back home to Buckland Common.

~ 7 ~
Dawdling Bugs, Dung Clamps – and Things that go Bump in the Night

WE HAD A RARE DO up at the village hall a couple of years back y'know. That wus old Miss Peacock's 50th h'anniversary in the Mothers Union. 'Course, she weren't a proper member. She wus what we calls a Honorary Member. Honorary members are all them old gels in the village what ain't never been married – what we calls 'near misses'.

They nearly made it – but not quite!

Mind you, they sowed their wild oats in the Springtime alright, but they somehow missed out on the harvest!

We got more honorary members than proper ones up here y'know, and old Miss Peacock wus one of 'em. Well, they said she wus in everything else in the village, so she might as well be in that!

Mind you, I can't see where the bit about honour comes into it. Well – she lost that years ago! That's right! You ask old Billy Puddick the Sexton about the times when him and her reckoned to be fire-watching up there at the Windmill. Ha! There wus some rare goings on up there during the war I can tell yer – them old Jerry bombs weren't the only things what wus coming down a night, and if that old Dawdling Bug what comed a'whistling over the top of the Windmill had been just a few minutes late, she'd have been a full time proper member of the Mothers Union!

But didn't that old Dawdling Bug make a row when that comed down – but that never went orf y'know, that never went orf! And where do you think that landed? Why, right next to Charley Buckley's corrugated h'outdoor sanitorium!

Me and old Harry Feathers wus walking by at the time – and didn't that make that old sani rattle!

"What wus that? What wus that?" shouted Harry. "S'alright," I says, "that's only old Charley," I says, "he always has a bit of trouble when he has onions for dinner."

But we soon found out that it weren't old Charley's onions making it rattle, because he comes a'galloping out of the front gate a'shouting his head orf!

"Quick, quick!" he hollers, "fetch out the Local Defence Volunteers* – there's a great big h'unexploded Dawdling Bug landed right next to me h'outdoor sanitorium!"

"Right!" I says, "you go and fetch 'em Harry," I says, "and I'll go and fetch Percy Lamkin. I can't see what good he can do, but I know he'd like to be here – and you be sure to tell them chaps to bring their gas-masks. I reckon they're really going to need them this time!"

But old Percy wouldn't come y'know.

"I can't leave my dung-clamp," he says, "not 'til my missus comes home."

He'd been having a bit of trouble with somebody pinching it y'know. He'd got an idea it wus the Civil Defence lot, filling up their sandbags with it, and using them for unarmed combat practice.

"Well!" I says, "I reckon we've as good as won the war then," I says, "if our lads are brave enough to risk their lives in mortal combat with a bagful of your bestest minure – well! I reckon them old Jerries have had it!"

Anyway, that weren't very long afore h'up comed the heroes of the hour, the Local Defence Volunteers, the good old L.D.V.'s – knowed throughout the villages as the 'Look, Duck and Vanish' Brigade!

He comed up on his bike y'know, with Harry on the crossbar.

"Well!" I says, "where's the rest of them then?"

"Up at the White Lion," says Harry, "when I told them there wus a h'unexploded Dawdling Bug comed down up the village, they wus all a'raring to go – but when I told them where it had comed down, they said they'd got a darts match."

So I says, "Well, why didn't you ask the Civil Defence then?"

"I did that," says Harry, "they got a darts match as well."

"Oh?" I says, "who are they playing then?"

"Why," he says, "the Local Defence Volunteers of course!"

"Ye'es," I says, "they would be wouldn't they!"

"Y'know," says Harry, "we could have a big upset here."

"You're right," I says, "if the L.D.V.'s win, they'll go to the top of the league!"

"No, no, not that," says Harry, "if that there thing goes orf, we could have a serious problem."

"Good lor!" I says, "I never thought of that."

"Yes!" says Harry, "if that Dawdling Bug h'explodes – we could have the worst disaster this village has ever knowed!"

**Local Defence Volunteers.* (L.D.V.'s for short), were the forerunners of the Home Guard during the 2nd World War 1939-1945. Nicknamed locally as 'The Look, Duck and Vanish Brigade'.

"Oh no!" I says, "you don't mean . . ."

"Yes I do," says Harry, "it means that Charley Buckley's h'outdoor sanitorium will be blown sky high!"

"Well," I says, "that can't be such a bad thing now can it!"

"But don't you see?" says old Harry, "if that happens – why, why then Charley Buckley will have to use someone else's!"

"Quick! Quick!" I says to the L.D.V. chap, "have you got any barbedy wire handy?"

"I got some in me saddlebag," he says, "are you going to throw a barbedy wired fantanglement round that old Dawdling Bug then?"

"No, that I ain't!" I says, "I'm going to throw it round my h'outdoor sanitorium – old Charley ain't using mine!"

"Well!" says the Look, Duck and Vanish chap, "Charley ain't as bad as all that is he?"

"You can tell he ain't a local chap, can't you?" I says to Harry. "Do you know mate," I says, "if our lot was to get somebody to take old Charley's h'outdoor sanitorium up in one of them there h'airy planes and tip it out over Germany – why, that'ud finish orf the war in about five minutes!"

"Well!" says the L.D.V. chap, "why ever don't you tell the Civil Defence about it then – they'd get somebody to do it."

"Go on with you," I says, "who are they going to get? There ain't a soul in the whole village brave enough to face what's in there! Why, even old Charley his-self has to go in backwards!"

"Well," says Harry, "what are we going to do about it then? We can't leave that old Dawdling Bug just a'laying there now can we."

"Constable Ayres," I says, "he's the chap to see – he'll know what to do!"

Well, old Harry went and fetched him y'know, but he weren't no help at all!

"Is it outside your sanitorium?" he says to old Charley, and Charley says, "Ar".

"Well," says Constable Ayres, a'licking the end of his pencil, "if that ain't claimed in three months, then you can have it!"

In the end, old Charley says that seeing as how he didn't really want it, he'd write to them old Jerries what had sent it over and ask them if they wanted it back. He said that seeing as how that ain't gone orf, they could use that again then – if they liked!

But somebody from the parish council got to hear about it, and sent old Percy Lamkin round to come and cart it away on his wheelbarrer – and that was the last we see'd of it.

Old Charley never heared no more from them old Jerries y'know, and Percy said it was a good job they didn't want it back anyway, he reckoned that would take him best part of a week to push that all the way back to Germany!

He wouldn't tell us what he'd done with it, but word soon got round the villages not to dig too deep in his dung clamp – and d'you know, old Percy's never lost no more minure not from that day to this!

'Course, that was in the days of Samuel Mortlock y'know, the bestest coffin maker we ever had, hoor – he couldn't half make them!

He had a notice outside his workshop y'know, that said:

SAMUEL MORTLOCK
Maker of the finest quality coffins.
Guaranteed to last a lifetime.

– Ar, and they did too! When you got yourself inside one of Samuel Mortlock's coffins, why, that was a real pleasure to be buried!

Well, I mind the time when Billy Puddick's old Dad was buried – ah, 50 year ago. He had a Samuel Mortlock coffin y'know – and he's still using it – well, as far as I know.

They used a few of Sam's old coffins for Home Guard Sentry Boxes during the war y'know – second-hand ones of course! They stood them outside the places where they thought them old Jerries was most likely to h'invade – y'know, places of national importance – so the Home Guard Captain h'ordered three of them – one each for the Rose and Crown, the Full Moon, and the White Lion. Well, they don't come much more important than that now do they!

'Course, they was never short of volunteers for guard duty after that. D'you know, they had that many – they had to draw straws for it!

But I shall never forget the first night that old coffin sentry box stood outside the Rose and Crown. Just by the front door it were. That was the same night as that old Dawdling Bug comed a'whistling over the top of the Windmill – y'know, what I've just been a'telling you about.

Old Sam delivered them in his hearse y'know – after dark, of course! Well, you don't want to put the wind up too many people now do you. I mean to say, it ain't very often you see three coffins in a hearse at the same time now is it. They see them – and folkses'll start thinking there's an endemic or summat!

Anyway, Percy Lamkin won the first night on duty outside the Rose and Crown, and he comed a'trundling up with his old wheelbarrer – he never goes anywhere without it y'know – parked it round the back of the pub, told the landlord he was on duty, and went and stood in the coffin – pitchfork at the ready!

Well, d'you know, he ain't been there above 20 minutes, when that comed on to rain – and all he'd got to keep his-self dry, was one of Charley Buckley's big old white flour sacks.

"Beggar this!" he says to his-self, "I'm getting soaked out here!" So he does no more than lays the coffin down, clambers inside, covers his-self over with the flour sack – and puts the lid on!

"Ah, that's better," he says, "I'll lay here while that leaves orf raining."

Well, he got that comfortable y'know – he must have dropped orf asleep, because the next thing he heard was that old Dawdling Bug a'kicking up an almighty terrible din, as that whistled over the top of the Windmill!

But you never see'd anything like what happened next – ar, and ain't never likely to – not in all your born days!

The lid of the coffin shot orf and clattered onto the cobblestones as old Percy sat bolt upright – still covered in the white flour sack, waving his arms about and shouting at the top of his voice, just as all the folkses comed a'piling out of the pub door to see what all the commotion was about.

'Course, when they see'd this apparition sitting bolt upright in a coffin – covered all over with a white shroud, waving its arms in the air, and moaning and groaning summat about "I'm a'getting all stiff laying in here!" – all hell was let loose!

There was folkses running here, there, and everywhere – screaming and shouting for all they was worth, and then suddenly, just as old Percy stood up and put one leg outside the coffin, they let out one h'almighty shriek, and all shot back into the pub again – slammed the door shut after them and bolted it fast! And d'you know, not one of them folkses dared to move out of the pub until daylight comed the next morning!

'Course, old Percy had put the coffin round the back of the pub, and gone home long before then, so they never did find out just what it was they saw the night before!

But the old landlord, well, he'd never knowed such times, not in all the years he'd been at the Rose and Crown. What with 30 or 40 of 'em all staying for bed and breakfast and that, he'd done very well for his-self – and d'you know, he were that pleased with old Percy, that every time he wus on sentry duty at the Rose and Crown, there wus always a pint of Old and Mild waiting for him in the bottom of the coffin.

They do say the old landlord sold more tots of brandy in that one night than he sold during the whole of the war – and they still does alright in here y'know, on account of what happened that night, because when old Percy showed the landlord the white flour sack what he covered his-self over with in that old coffin, he straightway give Percy four half-crowns! – one for the sack, and three more to keep his mouth shut!

'Course, the story travelled round the villages, and beyond, like wildfire y'know, as to how all them folkses in the Rose and Crown that fateful night heard this strange eerie screeching sound a'coming from out of the night sky – and how they all piled out of the pub to see what was a'going on – and how they were all frightened near to death by a phantom corpse covered all over with a ghostly white shroud, a'moaning and a'groaning and sitting bolt upright in an old coffin what had just dropped out of the sky – and how that had disappeared as quick as that come, just like that there! And do you know, to this very day, folkses still come up here from miles around, trying to catch a glimpse of the Ghost in the Coffin, what moans and groans, and gives out an eerie whistling screech – just like, just like an old war-time Dawdling Bug!

But by far the biggest attraction is in this old pub itself, and they come here in their droves y'know, just to have a look at the Ghostly White Shroud what still hangs behind the bar, where the old landlord put it all them years ago!

Ha! He reckoned as how that wus the bestest money he'd ever spent, when he gave old Percy three half-crowns to keep his mouth shut! And I wouldn't be surprised if he weren't right too!

. . . Ha, that's been a'hanging in that old glass cabinet behind the bar, under lock and key, for more than 50 year now – handed down from landlord to landlord. Well, that's their bread and butter ain't it!

They don't let anybody handle it, or get too close a look at it either! Well, I mean to say, that only wants one person to see what's wrote on the other side of it, and the story of the Ghostly White Shroud would, would vanish into thin air overnight! And we don't want that to happen now do we!

What's that you say? Am I going to tell you what's wrote on it then? Ooooh – no fears I am! That's a secret that even I has to keep quiet about! Besides, that story's been worth hundreds of pints to me over the years, and I wants to keep it that way!

My word, that's a lovely fire we got now ain't it? Seems a shame to leave it just now don't it! What's that you say? – another pint for another story? Well now, that's an offer I can't refuse. So what's it to be then? Ah yes – I'll tell you about the time Percy Lamkin got his-self tangled up with the Weights and Measures Man what comed over here all the way from Aylesbury . . .

Brusher Morley's story continues on page 76

~ 8 ~
In Ever Increasing Circles

PERCY LAMKIN, the Roadman, was sitting outside the Full Moon the other afternoon, along with a nice pint enjoying the sunshine, when the peace and serenity of that sublime moment was rudely and violently shattered by such a clattering and a banging, that he wondered what on earth was going on. He looked up, and who should it be but Brusher Morley and Miss Peacock, trundling a couple of clapped-out, back-firing, motorised lawnmowers along the road.

"Hoi!" he shouted – "where be you orf to then?"

"Down the Vale," replied Brusher, "we're goin' to get our mowers mended be that nice chap at the Poultry Farm."

"Hold on," Percy shouted, "I'll go and fetch mine – that needs . . . here, half a mo, chap at the Poultry Farm? Don't be silly – he don't know nothing about lawn mowers."

"Don't you believe it," said old Busher, "according to Miss Peacock 'ere, he knows all there is to know about 'em," – so with that, Percy went and gathered his mower from out of its shed, then all three set off down the road with even more clattering, banging, and backfiring.

But isn't it amazing how incredibly fast good news travels, because all along the entire length of the route to the newly discovered mechanised motor mower mender at the Poultry Farm, folks were standing three or four deep, all of them with a machine to mend, waiting to join in the queue – that was now fast approaching epidemic proportions – behind Brusher Morley, Percy Lamkin, and Miss Peacock – and d'you know, by the time they arrived at the top of the hill adjacent to the church, there must have been, at the very least, a hundred and fifty of them, with more and more folks joining on the end all along the way, swelling the ever increasing convoy to unprecedented dimensions, with every last one of them revving up their mowers as they trundled them along the road.

Down Hawridge Hill they went, snaking along The Vale heading for the Poultry Farm, creating a continuous crescendo of earsplitting noise, simultaneously kicking up a huge great dust cloud of gigantic proportions, that rose in the air for hundreds of feet. The ground beneath them, under immense pressure from the pounding of hundreds of motor mowers, was vibrating to such an extent, that it actually measured – as they discovered later – three points on the Richter Scale . . .

"What's a Richter Scale?" asked Percy afterwards in the Tap Room of the Rose and Crown.

"That's exactly like a set of steelyards*," smiled Brusher mischieviously, "only much bigger – they use 'em for weighing earthcakes y'know."

"How much does an earthcake weigh then?" queried Percy.

"About as much as five good-sized hayricks," came the reply, "give or take a few trusses."

"So what do they hang this 'ere Richter Scale on then?" said Percy. "That's got to be a pretty stout beam to hold five good-sized hayricks, ain't it?"

At this point, Brusher wisely introduced some genuine common sense to the conversation in his final reply . . .

"Shut up, Perce," he said.

Travellers in the Rose and Crown the same evening reckoned the noise was of such enormity, they could hear it quite clearly from ten miles away – and the huge great dust cloud of gigantic proportions could be seen from as far away as London! The convoy of motorised mowers, out of sight to the rest of the world, was causing widespread panic as the noise grew louder and louder, and the dust cloud rose higher and higher. Rumours, describing several major catastrophies in graphic detail, were rife, spreading like wildfire across the country. Questions were asked in the Houses of Parliament, dramatic headlines splashed over the front pages of all the national newspapers, and for days afterwards, the Hilltop Villages were swarming with armoured personnel carriers – hundreds of troops, all armed to the teeth – television cameras – reporters – and men with clip-boards from the Ministry-of-whoever-it-is

**Steelyards*. Invented 1639. An apparatus for weighing that has a short arm, taking the article to be weighed and a long graduated arm, along which a weight is moved until it balances. Usually suspended from a stout beam or joist. Mainly used on farms for weighing trusses of hay, straw etc.

that deals with such matters. Having had reports of a huge explosion, and a colossal convoy of mysterious motorised machinery moving down from the Hilltop Villages under cover of a massive camouflaging cloud of what-ever-it-was, they all reacted under the complete misapprehension that it was either an alien space landing, the start of a Third World War, or somebody had hijacked the brewer's dray which, of course, would have been really really serious.

And just as soon as he heard the tremendous noise, and saw the huge great cloud of dust rising, Major-General Rivington-Pike (retired) was dashing about – as fast as anybody can dash about at the age of ninety three – trying to mobilize the few remaining ex-members of the Local Defence Volunteers . . . but he couldn't find any, which wasn't too surprising really, as they were all down The Vale trying to get their mowers mended!

However, all that, of course, is quite another story.

When Brusher, Percy, and Miss Peacock, who were leading the way, eventually arrived at the Poultry Farm, the great long snaky convoy of mowers stretched out behind them as far as the eye could see. There were literally thousands of them! The chap from the Poultry Farm was standing at his gate, absolutely aghast at the awesome spectacle that confronted him, along with the rest of the villagers who had rushed out to see what all the commotion was about.

"I say," asked the chap, very politely under the circumstances, "what do you lot reckon you're doing here with all them there old mowers? The scrap yard's along the road y'know."

"Scrap yard?" cried Brusher indignantly, "old mowers? Them's ain't just any old mowers, them's our old mowers, and we've brought 'em all the way down 'ere from Buckland Common for you to mend."

"Mend?" replied the chap in astonishment. "*Mend?* I don't mend mowers!"

"There!" exclaimed Percy Lamkin, "I told you, didn't I, we're wasting our time down 'ere."

"Hold on," said Brusher, "hold on a minute. What d'you mean you don't mend mowers – you're in the Rotary Club ain't yer?"

"I most certainly am," replied the chap with some pride, puffing out his chest most importantly. "Not only am I in the Rotary Club, I also happen to be the Secretary and General Factotum."

"General Factotum!" whispered Percy to Miss Peacock, "d'you think he's anything to do with Major-General Rivington-Pike?"

"More'n likely," she replied, "probably from the same regiment. Rivington-Pike can't mend mowers either!"

" . . . and this gentleman with me," continued the chap, gesticulating to a man dressed in a very nice suit, "happens to to be the President. But what's that got to do with it?"

"President?" whispered Percy again, "President? Do you think he's come all the way from foreign parts then – even – even from . . . America?"

"Definitely," Miss Peacock answered, "he's most definitely come from foreign parts. He certainly isn't a local that's for sure – there's nobody round here got a suit like that! He's the President from America that's what he is – yes, yes, that's it, the President from America. These Rotary people always reckon to be pretty important. So if the President from America has come all the way over here just to see them – especially in his best suit – then I suppose they must be."

"What's that got to do with it?" cried Brusher. "What's that got to do with it? Why, look at all these mowers – there's thousands of 'em there are – and every last one on 'em's a Rotary. We've come 'ere to join your club – that's what's got to do with it – so's we can get 'em all mended."

"Join our club?" the fellow cried in disbelief. "You lot! Join our club? Hooor, I don't know about that, we're pretty particular y'know, we don't have just any old body in our club!"

"Well," blurted Percy Lamkin, "you're in it."

" – and how about 'im," said Brusher, nodding towards the President from America, "how the hell did 'e get in, I bet 'e can't mend a mower."

"Now look here," replied the chap from the Poultry Farm, raising his voice a bit, "I told you before, the Rotary Club don't mend Rotary mowers!"

"Well," asked Billy Puddick, "what sort of mowers do you mend then?"

"I keep telling you!" bellowed the chap, "*We don't mend mowers! We don't mend mowers – rotarys or otherwise!* Us chaps in the Rotary Club go about doing good for the local community – and beyond! We've got clubs everywhere y'know, ar, all over the world and . . . and far away."

"So why ain't you got one in Buckland Common then?" piped up Miss Peacock.

"I didn't mean that far away," said the chap, "besides, by the looks of you lot, and these old mowers, I reckon that's a different world altogether up there."

"Well!" Brusher replied rather indignantly, "anybody would think we were foreigners."

"What's a foreigners?" asked Percy Lamkin.

"I dunno," answered Brusher, "I just heard it in the Rose and Crown one time – it's French y'know."

Well, when he said that, the chap from The Vale got quite excited, because all of a sudden he blurted out "Parlez-vous français? parlez-vous français?"

"Beg pardon?" said Brusher.

"Parlez-vous français?" he repeated, "parlez-vous français?"

"Tell 'im – je ne sais pas," whispered Miss Peacock, "tell 'im – je ne sais pas."

"Je ne say pas!" shouted Brusher, "je ne say pas!"

"Bless me!" cried the chap from The Vale, "whatever might that mean then?"

"Well!" replied Brusher, with some agitation, "I don't know!"

"Well done, well done," said the President from America, breaking his silence at last. "Not only can he speak French, he can interpret it as well. Do y'know," he said, "we've been looking everywhere for somebody able to speak the language, and interpret it into the bargain – and you're the first one we've come across. How would you like to do a little job for us?"

" 'Old on," said Percy, butting in, " 'old on! – we asked first, remember? What about our mowers?"

"Alright," answered the President from America, "you do the French job for us, and we'll see to all your mowers."

"Haaaa," exclaimed Percy, "now you're talking our language."

"Good man," said the President. "Now then," he started to explain, "we're having our dinner tomorrow night . . . "

"Tomorrow night?" interrupted Brusher incredulously, "tomorrow night? You mean you got to wait until then? Blimey – I wouldn't put up with that mate. I wants mine when I gets 'ome every night else there'll be trouble!"

"No, no," said the President, "let me finish what I was saying. It's the Annual Dinner of the local Rotary Club tomorrow night. We have one every year y'know, but this year, we're having some French folks over. The only snag is, we need a speaker, y'know, one as can speak the language, and you fit the bill just nicely. I might add that there will be free beer and dinner for you and a couple of friends. So, what d'you say?

"Tell 'im – oui oui Monsieur," whispered Miss Peacock, licking her lips, on account she could see a free meal looming. "Tell him – oui oui Monsieur, et merci beaucoup."

"Wee wee M'sewer," repeated Brusher, "and a mercy bouquet I'm sure."

"Well done, well done!" exclaimed the President. "Just present yourselves to the man on the door down at the hall tomorrow night, tell him who you are, and he'll let you in."

Well, getting down to the hall was easy enough, but actually getting into it was a different matter altogether. The old doorman just wouldn't let them in, not on any account.

"Ho no no no no no!" he cried, "I can't let any old personage in 'ere without some means of h'identification – that's more'n me jobs worth – what 'ave you got to show me?"

"I've got me old Dad's cap on," said Percy Lamkin, "with his name in it."

". . . and I got an old moleskin shirt on," Brusher said, "that's got his Dad's name in it too."

"I see," remarked the doorman, turning to Miss Peacock, "we're gettin' lower by the minute ain't we, I suppose your credentials are in your knickers then?"

"They might be," Miss Peacock replied quite pleasantly, "then again they might not be – *and even if they were!"* she bellowed *"I certainly wouldn't show 'em to you – me credentials are strictly private – how dare you!"* and before he knew what was happening, she walloped him one round the earhole with her handbag . . . "and just who do you think you are calling me an old personage!? Take that!" and more blows rained down on the unfortunate doorman.

"Oooooh!" he hollered, "there weren't no need for that – I think I'll by-pass your credentials if you let me 'ave a little look at your references," upon which, he smartly received a double wallop round the other earhole with the same handbag for his trouble.

"Oooooh!" he hollered again, "Oooooooh!" and then, with both hands clutching his earholes, leaving himself completely unprotected he cried, "alright Missus, alright, I give up – I'll let you in if you just let me 'ave a quick look at your curriculum vitae."

Well, well, that done it! All hell was let loose then, with Miss Peacock on the brink of explosion. She let out one almighty shriek, and laid into the poor old doorman something terrible, and the last they saw of them was when the doorman – doubled up with pain and clutching his own curriculum vitae – rushed through the front door with Miss Peacock, whirling her handbag round her head like a Mexican Bolas*, in hot pursuit.

"I'll give you credentials," she bellowed, "and references, and curriculum vitae – take that, and that, and that!" as they rushed through a patch of prickly roses, before plunging headlong into a bed of Forget-me-nots.

As for Billy and Brusher, well, they just walked into the hall and had a wonderful evening. Very sensibly, the multilingual Brusher decided that he didn't really ought to speak in a foreign tongue on this occasion, seeing as how his interpreter was otherwise engaged, so instead, he just stood up and told the Rotary people all about Henry Billinge, and his encounter with Annie Lovegrove and her cricket bat, up at the post office in Buckland Common.

He could have spoken in French after all. Nobody would have been any the wiser. His country dialect was so broad, it might just as well have been a foreign language anyway – because not one soul attending that evening understood a word he said!

. . . We're still waiting for our lawnmowers y'know – they're certainly taking their time mending them. I'm just beginning to wonder if they're ever going to men. . . *here!*. . .

. . . Hold on – *hold on a minute!* . . .

Where did he say that scrap yard was . . . ?"

**Bolas*. Esp. South America. A missile consisting of two or more balls connected by a strong cord, swung round the head and discharged so as to wind round and entangle cattle etc.

~ 9 ~
A Barrerload of Trouble

THAT ALL STARTED the day the old Road Foreman tried to give Percy Lamkin a brand new wheelbarrer. Well, you should've seen it! That wus a blessed great thing. If that'd been much bigger, that would've needed shafts. Old Percy took one look at it, and unbuckled his belt. He'd got his trousers halfway down to his knees before the old Road Foreman see'd him.

"Hey, hey, hey, Lamkin!" shouted the old Road Foreman, "what d'you think you're a'doing?"

"Doing?" says old Percy, "why, I'm taking me trousers orf – if I've got to work like an horse, I might as well look like one!"

Well, we had to laugh, and y'know, that old barrer never did get used. You could tell just by looking at it, that'ud need a good man to push it, so you might know that were a waste of time bringing it into a council yard!

Freddie Carter comed into the yard just then, a'looking for a job.

"Sorry Freddie," says the old Road Foreman, "I ain't hardly got enough work for me own men."

"Go on with yer," says Freddie, "the little bit I'll do won't make no difference!"

"Ah well, that's alright then," says the old Road Foreman, "you can start right away!"

Not like poor old Teddy Medders. Worked on the Council for nigh on seventy-five year y'know – man and boy – then they went and give him the sack 'cause they said he wus too old!

"Well – dang that then!" says old Teddy, "if I'd knowed that weren't going to be a regular job, I wouldn't have started in the first place!"

Then Percy Lamkin went and got his-self into a bit of bother. He'd just cleared up a few heaps of 'orse minure from along the road – left over from the night before – when a chap on a bike stopped right in front of him.

"Morning," says the chap on the bike, rubbing his hands together, "that's fresh this morning isn't it."

"No," says Percy, "that's yesterday's."

"No, no," says the chap, "it's cold isn't it!"

"Well, so would you be," says Percy, "if you'd been laying in the middle of the road all night like this has!"

"Right, that's enough!" says the chap, fetching out his notebook, "I'm Weights and Measures from Aylesbury."

"How d'you do," says Percy, "I'm Percy and Lamkin from Buckland Common."

"Now then," says the chap, a'licking the end of his pencil, "that there stuff in that there wheelbarrer – is it yours?"

"No," says Percy, "I always go afore I comes to work in the morning."

"I didn't mean that!" says the chap, "I mean't – how did you come by it?"

"I didn't come by it," says Percy, "you can see I picked it up."

"Well, was there a ticket with it?" says the chap.

"Not that I know of," says Percy, "but then – I never looked that close."

"Ha!" says the chap, a'licking the end of his pencil, "no ticket eh? Don't you ever pick this stuff up with a ticket?"

"Well – no," says Percy, "I always uses me shovel."

"Now look here," says the chap, "don't you know you must have a ticket for it – how do you expect us chaps to know where it's come from?"

"Well!" says Percy, "I thought everybody knowed where this stuff comes from."

"Oh?" says the chap, "does it always come out from the same place then?"

"Well – yes," says Percy, scratching his head, "I've never see'd it come out from anywhere else yet awhile."

By this time, the chap from Weights and Measures wus getting a bit hot under the collar y'know, and he raised his voice a bit!

"Right!" he says, "you say it isn't yours – you haven't got a ticket for it – and it all comes out of the same place. Well, where does it come from then – where does it come from then?"

"Orses!" says Percy – nice and slow like, "Orses!"

Well y'know – they don't half talk funny up here in the villages be times, and sometimes their O's sound a bit like A's – and when Percy said 'Orses!' – well, that didn't sound a bit like 'Orses' to a well-spoken chap fresh out from the Weights and Measures office!

"Ooooooh!" says the chap, "there's no need for that sort of talk. I've a good mind to go and fetch the Constable and have you charged!"

"Ha! – you got that the wrong way round," says Percy, "that's him what's being charged – this here barrerful's for him."

"Ha!" says the chap, a'licking the end of his pencil, "delivering it as well are you? And without a ticket – now I've really gotcher! Now then," he says, "what's the weight of a barrerful of minure?"

"About 10 minutes," says Percy.

"I see," says the chap, "no ticket and not weighed – I reckon I'm going to have to fine you."

"What for?" says Percy, "I ain't lost."

"Right!" says the chap, "that does it! I'm afraid I shall have to ask you to turn that barrerful over to me."

"Righto," says Percy, and before this chap realised what he'd said, Percy had h'upped with the handles – and there he wus standing knee-deep in four pennyworth of last night's horse minure, and do you know – old Percy's never had no more trouble with Weights and Measures chaps not from that day to this!

Billy Elliott fell off a ladder in the Council yard a while back. Percy Lamkin see'd it all happen y'know. He said he ain't seen old Billy move so fast in years. 25 foot he fell – but he weren't half lucky. Well, if the ground ain't have stopped him there's no telling how far he would've gone. Percy knowed that wus 25 foot. He counted the rungs as old Billy hit 'em on the way down!

The old Road Foreman comed a'rushing across just as he wus a'falling y'know – but he wus too late, and poor old Billy fell on his broom and hurt his leg!

"Oh dear, oh dear!" says the old Road Foreman, a'looking at Billy's leg, "ain't this terrible – do you reckon he's broke it?"

"Course he has!" says Percy, a'looking at the broom, "clean in half!"

"Oh dear, oh dear!" says the old Road Foreman, "whatever shall we do – whatever shall we do?"

"Do?" says Percy, "do? Why – fetch him another one – there's plenty more in the toolshed. But y'know," he says, "that's just like old Billy ain't it – thinking of hisself again."

"How d'you mean?" says the old Road Foreman.

"Well," says Percy, "if he'd a'fell off the other side of the ladder, he'd a'broke mine!"

Middle of the morning that happened y'know – right after lunch-time. Percy weren't half upset about that y'know. He reckoned if old Billy had fell off before lunchtime, they could've had his sandwiches!

But he's like that is Percy y'know – ain't got no time for folkses what ain't well – and he never goes to anybody's funeral.

"Why should I?" he says, "they won't be coming to mine!"

Freddie Carter had a rare job an' all one time y'know. The old Road Foreman told him to go and paint old Mother Poulton's garden gate. She'd got a sign nailed on that – only old Freddie being a bit shortsighted an' that – well, he never see'd it until that wus too late, and he painted right over the top of it.

Hor, weren't old Mother Poulton wild!

"Now look what you've been and gorn and done!" she bellered at poor old Freddie, "why don't you be more careful," she says – wiping the paint off the gate with Freddie's apron. "Now you do it agin – properly this time!"

"Righto," says old Freddie, a'looking a bit closer at the sign, "I'd better see what that says then – hmm – 'Beware of the Dog'," he says, "ah well – I can see what's wrong with it now," he says, "you've got it spelt wrong!"

"Have I?" she says.

"Yees," says old Freddie, and he took a'hold of his paint brush, crossed out 'Dog' – and put 'Bitch' instead!

Ha – that had her!

Not like old Henry Padfield. He used to empty all the h'outdoor sanitorium buckets in the village y'know. One of the bestest jobs on the Council that wus, on account as he wus his own boss – more or less anyway. There weren't many folks about as told old Hener what to do that's for sure – least of all the old Road Foreman. Well, they couldn't get close enough could they! They wus all driven back be the smell!

On the other hand, the old Road Foreman hadn't got no need to get all that close. If at any time he couldn't find old Hener, he used to stand in the middle of the cricket pitch up there on Hawridge Common, take a wonderful swing of anaesthetic out of a whiskey bottle – take two or three deep sniffs – and he could pinpoint old Hener to within ten foot – even down to which house he wus at, and whose it wus!

Ha! – takes a fair bit of skill that does, and years of experience. That's why the job of village Road Foreman carries a five year apprenticeship with it y'know – with a one day a week sniffer course on the cricket pitch!

Y'know, there ain't many folkses as realise just what goes into the makings of a Road Foreman. That ain't all just riding around on a motor-bike and sidecar a'listening out for squeaky wheels on Roadmen's wheelbarrers, telling chaps what to do, and making a general nuisance of yourself!

Ar, there's a lot more to it than that – and if you're a'thinking of applying for the job, then remember this. If you're deaf – or can't smell a h'outdoor sanitorium bucket at a distance of half a mile from the middle of Hawridge cricket pitch – and get it right to within ten foot – and you ain't any good at making a general nuisance of yourself – then you're wasting your time!

But where wus I? Oh yes, I remember.

While all this wus a'going on of course, old Hener wus steadily going round a'hemptying all the sani buckets. They used to get emptied once every eight weeks y'know – whether they needed it or not!

He never had any trouble with h'emptying them y'know, all except one – Charley Buckley's up there at the Windmill! Even he couldn't get anywhere near that one!

Hor, that wus a terror that wus – real fearsome! That had been handed down y'know – just like my old barrer wus all them years ago.

Old Charley wus proud of that – never been h'emptied in its life has that old sani! Charley reckoned there weren't a chap on the Council workforce as could hold his breath for long enough to do the job – and I wouldn't be surprised if he ain't right too!

They used to say y'know, if you wus to strike a match in there, that'ud blow the whole lot sky-high. Henery Padfield said he would never dare go in there with his pipe alight – but old Charley said he would never go in if his weren't!

Old Dr Simmons, the Home Guard Captain, used that old sani during the war for the Home Guard medical test y'know. He used to make the new recruits go in there one at a time – without a gas-mask – and if they could stay in there for two minutes without a'hollering to come out, they wus passed A1 – and mentioned in the Parish Magazine!

Dr Simmons said he would've had them 'Mentioned in Dispatches' – only he never knowed who printed that.

They reckoned as how we wus the only Home Guard platoon in the whole of Buckinghamshire, where the chaps that passed their medical A1 – were straightway sent home on two weeks sick leave!

You can't get much braver than that now can you! . . . So you see – there's more to Council work than first meets the eye ain't there! What's that you say? Did them old sani's really smell as bad as all that? I can see I shall have to tell you all about the time when old Dr Simmons had more that he bargained for, on account of h'out-door sanitoriums – and certainly more than he could handle, when he give Mary Feathers, the Dung Carter's wife, a special prescription!

But all that will have to be next time, on account the fire's nearly gone out, and be the looks of that old clock, that's about time we all wus.

Goodnight all . . .

Brusher Morley's story continues on page 88

~10~ Who Needs a Motey-car when you've got a Wheelbarrow

THAT ALL STARTED the day Miss Arkley pinned a card on the church notice-board advertising for a handyman.

Percy Lamkin was the only one who had enough courage to reply. He didn't go all by himself of course, oh dearie me no – he weren't that brave! Well, I know for a fact, there ain't a chap yet has ever come away from Miss Arkley's cottage, without first having felt the full force of a few wallops round the earholes – so rather than go by himself, he took his wheelbarrow along, just for company like – well, more for protection really. He reckoned it out like this, if he could keep the wheelbarrow between himself and Miss Arkley, he stood a reasonable chance of coming away from there without having his earholes seriously warmed!

He learned that at school y'know – about the only thing he ever did learn! Well, when Miss Arkley was Headmistress, that was the first thing everybody learned at school – always keep summat between yourself and Miss Arkley – that was *the* golden rule, a rule to be observed at all times, and it still is, even to this very day – ar, 50 years on – and you break it at your peril, unless you fancy having your earholes warmed!

She used to sing as she walloped your earholes y'know 'The Hallelujah Chorus' it were – that was the one. Hor! – she couldn't half sing y'know, and her timing couldn't be faulted, with every wallop landing in perfect time to every Hallelujah! When she comed to the bit where there were four or five Hallelujahs in quick succession, her old hands moved like greased lightening! The faster she sang of course, the faster the wallops! There was never a chance of us chaps ever forgetting the tune y'know, because for days after they had been walloped, your earholes were still singing it! And that's the reason, of course, as to why, even though it all happened 50 or so years ago, 'The Hallelujah Chorus' is definitely not everybody's favourite!

There's no getting away from it – she was, and still is, a past master at Hallelujah earhole walloping! It's the uncertainty y'know. Waiting for one to land is like waiting for the second coming of the Lord really. Well, you know it's going to happen sometime, but you never know when, so you've got to be prepared for it!

Ar, old habits die hard with Miss Arkley – and even more so if you were an ex-pupil, as most of the folks are as live up here!

"Morning Miss," says Percy, doffing his cap as she answered the door of her cottage up there on Hawridge Common, making sure of course to keep his distance on the far side of his wheelbarrow, "I hear you're looking for a handyman."

"Yes," she barked, eyeing Percy up and down, "so why are you wasting your time applying for the job then? I know all about you Lamkin – can't do this and won't do that. What makes you think you're so handy?"

"Well, I must be," says Percy, "I only lives just round the corner."

"Ha!" she says, "about the only thing handy about you," she says, nodding towards the wheelbarrow, "is that you've got your own transport."

"Well," says Percy, still standing on the far side of his wheelbarrow, "do you want me or not?"

"Tell you what," says Miss Arkley, "I'll give you a trial. I need a new name for my cottage, and I wants it nailed on to me gate – but I can't think what to call it yet – I don't suppose you have any suggestions?"

"Oh ar," says Percy, "I can think of plenty . . . " but he bit his tongue just in time – which was just as well really, because the names that he was about to suggest, would have resulted in not only having both earholes well and truly 'Hallelujah Chorused', she would probably have conducted the rest of the tune on the seat of his trousers with her broomstick for good measure!

Just at that moment Miss Arkley put the handyman's interview to one side, and pointed across the garden.

"What's them little old birds over there Lamkin?" she whispered.

"What, them ones a'twittering on that clump of teazels?" says Percy. "Why, them's Goldfinches Miss, they've been around here for years they have – always a'twittering they be y'know."

"That's it!" she cried. "That's it! That's what I shall call my cottage."

"What – Goldfinches?" says Percy.

"No, no, no," she says, "Twitterings – The Old Twitterings – that's what I shall call it – The Old Twitterings. What a lovely name that is!"

"Hor, I'm beggared," says Percy, "how the hell do you spell that then?"

And you can quite understand him asking really. Well, I mean to say – he had a hard enough job to write his name, never mind trying to spell 'twitterings'.

"How do you spell it, how do you spell it?" she bellers, "why – T W I . . . "

"No, no, no," says Percy, fetching out his pencil, "lets start at the beginning – how do you spell 'old'?"

Bit of a loner was Percy – kept himself pretty much to himself. The bestest friend he ever had was that old wheelbarrow y'know – through thick and thin, in good times or in bad, that always stood by him. Like any true friend, that was always there if he wanted it. But not this time, because d'you know, he'd got that interested in them little old twittering Goldfinches, that he completely forgot the golden rule – and before he realised what he was doing, he'd wandered from the safety of his bestest friend, and strayed into no-man's land on the wrong side of the barrer! Well, you couldn't blame the barrer now could you! That was still stood standing there like any true friend would, offering him the safe haven he so desperately needed. He tried to scrabble back – but he was too late! Miss Arkley had already got the range on his earholes!

"What!" she bellowed. "What! You mean you can't even spell 'old' – after all these years?"

"Well, I used to once," says Percy, "but now I can't remember."

"You used to once but now you can't remember?" she cried, and Percy detected a definite lilt in her voice, which, from bitter experience of his schoolboy days, told him that she was building up to something much much bigger – and his earholes started to twitch, just as they used to some 50 years ago!

"You used to once but now you can't remember? Well – remember this then!" and, with a great cry of triumph, she launched into the attack with her deep contralto voice, singing the battle hymn of her School Marm days – the magnificent opening bars of the 'Hallelujah Chorus' – and poor old Percy found himself on the wrong end of a severe earhole warming!

"Halle-*wallop*, Halle-*wallop*, Halle-*wallop*, Halle-*wallop*, Ha-ley-*wallop* – Halle*wallop*!" Her timing was exquisite, with every wallop landing on Percy's earholes in perfect time to the singing. Ar, and she never held back none either! You can forget all about your soft back-pedalling double PP Pianissimo – all her Hallewallops were delivered with an earsplitting triple FFF Fortissimo!

"Ooooooh!" cried Percy, "ooooooh! – whatever were they for then?"

"One for being ignorant," shouted Miss Arkley, "and all the rest for not paying attention when you were at school!"

"Now then," she says, "let's see about this sign for the gate – and seeing as how you can't spell, I shall write it out for you. All you have to do is paint it on a bit of wood and nail it to the gate."

Well, old Percy did that, but 'The Old Twitterings' ain't half a long name y'know, and when he'd done the painting bit of the job, he finished up with a sign about 6 foot long. Now that was a lucky job Miss Arkley had a set of double gates to her cottage, else I don't know what he would've done, because as it was, that old sign stretched right across the pair of them. Without giving it a second thought, he took a'hold of his hammer and nailed the sign in position. Then, of course, like the wonderful chap he is – he tried to open the gate!

He stood there for a minute or two scratching his head, wondering why he couldn't get it open! Then it suddenly dawned on him!

"Oooh I'm beggared!" he said. "Now what am I going to do – she'll be down here in a minute or two! Ha – I know," he says, "I'll cut the thing in half between the two gates." So he did, and d'you know, due partly to the unfortunate siting of the sign, and Percy not being able to spell all that well, the cut-off point just happened to be in the worst possible place – right between the two TT's of Twitterings!

Little did he know it, but exactly 45 seconds after he'd done the deed, he was going to wish – and not for the first time that day – he was going to wish he'd paid more attention when he was at school!

Yet again, he stepped away from the safety of his wheelbarrow, this time to admire his handiwork, just as Miss Arkley arrived on the scene!

"Ha," says Percy, feeling quite pleased with himself, "that looks nice don't it!" And so that did – until she opened the blessed gate, which of course left 'terings' on one side, and 'The Old Twit' on the other!

And so it came to pass, for the second time that day, the tranquil air that hanged above 'The Old Twit' cottage was once again alive with the awesome rendition of the 'Hallewallop Chorus' – with the usual Triple FFF Fortissimo accompaniment!

. . . "Come on Lamkin," she bellows at poor old Percy, "never mind rubbing your earholes and feeling sorry for yourself. I've got another little job lined up for you – and that's a pity that there old wheelbarrow of yours isn't a motey-car – perhaps it would move a bit faster then!"

Meanwhile, round at the church, the old Vicar was perched on the top rung of a pair of steps, stretching to fix a notice on the church notice-board. Seeing as how he was a bit short in the leg, and the steps weren't very tall, he was having to stand on tiptoe! He was just at the very limit of his reach, when Percy Lamkin comed puffing and panting round the corner pushing his wheelbarrow, piled up high with an old bed and a blessed great mattress, what he was taking down to the dump for Miss Arkley.

He saw the old Vicar a split second too late! He tried to take evasive action, but just caught the steps with the barrer.

"Oh my Lord," shouted the Vicar, staggering on the top rung, as the steps collapsed beneath him. "Save me, save me!"

Well, you wouldn't believe it, and he couldn't have timed it better had he tried. He somersaulted off the steps, and landed right in the middle of Miss Arkley's mattress as nice as you like!

As he lay there trying to regain his composure – completely none the worse for his ordeal – the notice what he'd been trying to pin up on the board, came fluttering gently down and landed right in his lap – and do you know what that said? Well, I'll tell you . . .

ANYONE WHO CALLS UPON THE NAME OF THE LORD, SHALL BE SAVED!

. . . it said.

"What do you think of that Lamkin?" cried the old Vicar, as he scrambled off the mattress waving the notice above his head. "What do you think of that! That's the power of prayer that is! The good Lord has just saved me from serious injury."

"How d'you mean?" says Percy, "the good Lord has saved you – it was me who was pushing the blessed wheelbarrow!"

"Ha – that's as maybe," says the old Vicar, "but the good Lord had his hand upon it."

"If he did," says old Percy, "then he must have been just leaning – because he certainly weren't pushing!"

"What we've witnessed here today Lamkin," says the old Vicar, "is nothing short of a miracle – the Good Lord himself placed that old bed and mattress on your wheelbarrow!"

"If that's the case," says Percy, "perhaps he could perform another one and give me a hand off with it – that beggar ain't half heavy!"

"I say," says the old Vicar, giving the mattress a prod, "that's a better bed than mine – what are you going to do with it?"

"I'm taking it down to the dump,"says Percy.

"Down to the dump? Down to the dump?" says the old Vicar, "I'll give you a pound for it!"

"What?" says Percy, "a pound?"

"Alright, alright," says the old Vicar, "tell you what I'll do, give me a hand upstairs with it, cart me old one away – and I'll give you two pounds."

"What – two pounds?" says Percy, "You'll give me two pounds out of your own pocket? Now that really is a miracle!"

. . . As he wandered down to the dump with two pounds in his pocket, and the old Vicar's mattress and bed perched on his barrer, he had the most wonderful flash of inspiration. He didn't know it at the time – but there was about to be an enormous change in his life for the better . . .

When Percy arrived back at 'The Old Twit' cottage, Miss Arkley came out to meet him – still fuming over her sign! She started off at Percy again, and was just going to launch into the 'Hallewallop Chorus' when Percy held up his hand!

"Hold on!" he says, "Hold on! That's enough of that – I wants a word with you!"

Well, Miss Arkley couldn't believe what she was hearing – nobody had ever stood up to her before, and she'd never ever been spoken to like that before not in all her born days!

"I'm listening Lamkin," she fumed, "and it better be good!"

With that, Percy whispered something in her ear, and suddenly, all the colour seemed to drain from her face and, from that moment on, her attitude towards Percy completely changed. There was an air of quiet resignation about her person, as she struggled to come to terms with whatever it was Percy had whispered to her.

"Well?" says Percy, "well – what d'you say?"

She drew herself up to her full height – and nodded.

"So be it Lamkin," she said, "so be it."

. . . And so it was then, they came to a compromised agreement. Miss Arkley gave Percy the part-time job as her handyman, agreed to teach him to read and write, and best of all, promised faithfully not to Hallewallop his earholes ever again – whilst Percy for his part of the bargain, crossing his heart and hoping to die, promised never to tell a living soul, that the old Vicar was sleeping in her bed!

So you see – from the anguish of animosity, came the flower of friendship. In fact, over the ensuing years Miss Arkley and Percy became good friends – and to this very day, the old Vicar still can't make out why Miss Arkley gives him a sweet smile and a knowing wave when she sits in the front pew up at St Mary's every Sunday morning!

Percy walked away from Miss Arkley's cottage that evening with a jaunty spring in his step. As he mulled over the events of the day, he realised just how much of his good fortune he owed to his faithful wheelbarrow. True, it didn't save him from a couple of Hallewallopings – they were his own fault for not remembering the golden rule! – but for the most part, his wheelbarrow had been instrumental in everything that had happened that day.

He glanced down at his bestest friend. The paintwork was all scratched and pitted, and the wheel squeaked – as all good barrer wheels do. He thought he might get a tin of Council green paint and give it a freshen up sometime. The Vicar's two pounds in loose change jangled in his pocket, as the wheelbarrow took it and himself ever nearer to the Rose and Crown.

His mind drifted back to 'The Old Twit' cottage. What was it Miss Arkley had said? "It's a pity that there old wheelbarrow of yours ain't a motey-car?"

"Ha!" he shouted at the top of his voice, *"if it had have been, we wouldn't have knocked the old Vicar off his perch would we, and none of this would never have happened!"* and with that emphatic remark, all his pent up emotions finally caught up with him. He couldn't contain himself any longer!

"Ha! ha! ha!" he chortled, as he danced a happy jig in the middle of the road. "Ha! ha! ha! *Who needs a motey-car, when your bestest friend's a wheelbarrow!*"

With these immortal words he burst into song, and, giving it a double double helping of triple FFF Fortissimo – the joyous tones of the 'Hallewallop Chorus' once again reverberated the length and breadth of Hawridge Common. It lingered on in the tranquil evening air, long after Percy had parked his wheelbarrow and disappeared into the Tap Room of the Rose and Crown.

So think on this . . .

Next time you're singing in the 'Hallewallop Chorus' – don't forget to take your wheelbarrow with you. That might be an encumbrance getting it up the steps into the church, but you never know – that might well turn out to be *your* bestest friend!

~11~
All Garlic and Gas-mask

'ERE, HOLD ON! – I ain't finished with that yet! What's that you say? You wants to fill it up again? Well now, that's very civil of you – yes, same agin thanks – Old and Mild – which is more than can be said for old Henery Padfield! Old he may be – but mild he never wus!

When you had the job of h'outdoor sanitorium bucket emptier for as long as he did – well, let me tell you all about it . . .

. . . It wus the time I got stuck behind some old dodderer a'driving a farm-cart. I thought to myself I thought – "I'm a'going to pass this old josser," so I stuck me hand out to overtake him – you know, like you do. Well, I never give it a thought y'know. I wus going that fast, I got into a speed wobble, lost control, and finished up on me backside in the ditch.

I never hurt meself much – but stone me – you should've seen me wheelbarrer!

Henery Padfield comed across to see if I wus alright. He put down the h'outdoor sanitorium bucket what he wus a'carrying to give me a hand up.

Phooor! – didn't he smell! I wus feeling a bit groggy when he comed across, but one whiff of old Hener, and in no time at all I wus feeling a lot worse!

You knows old Hener don't you? You must have seen him about – he's the chap as h'empties the h'outdoor sanitorium buckets for the Council – ar – one-handed! Remember him now don't you? Course you do – holds the bucket in one hand, and his nose with the other! Been with the Council 45 years he has. Worked for 30 of 'em! He's still at it y'know – and once a month regular as clockwork, whether that needs emptying or not, he carries his own sani-bucket down to the allotments, and spreads it on his garden.

Good old Hener – always did like to get his own back!

I mind when I wus talking to him one time up there by the cricket pitch on Hawridge Common – during the war it were. Mind you, I knowed he wus on the cricket pitch a long while before I got there. Well, you can tell easy enough – that there stuff don't half carry y'know. You can see it a'rising – and that wus a good 15 minutes after that before I clapped eyes on him. There he wus, sat on a h'outdoor sanitorium bucket, having his lunch! Well, he has to sit on summat don't he – and do you know what he wus a'doing? Well, I'll tell you. He'd got a'hold of the biggest onion you'd ever seen in your life, and he wus eating that just like you or me would eat an apple.

"Hoooor!" I says, "don't you smell bad enough already?" I says, "whatever are you doing eating that almighty onion?"

"Ah well", he says, "I've got the makings of a fearful monster of a cold a'coming – this is going to keep it off!"

So I says, "Yes," I says, "and everybody else and all!"

"Then tonight," he says, "when I gets home, I rubs meself all over with garlic, and come the morning," he says, "that old cold will have left me and gone."

"Blimey!" says Percy Lamkin, who wus just a'going past with his wheelbarrer – he never goes anywhere without it y'know, "if garlic and onions gets rid of nasty things as quick as that, I'll give that a go myself tonight I know! Just think what that could do for me! Hooor, I hope it works, I hope it works!" and off he went with his barrer.

"Well," says old Hener, "whatever did he mean by that? He ain't got a fearful monster of a cold has he!"

So I says "No," I says, "but you've seen his missus ain't you?" Then I says "y'know Hener," I says, "I reckon a bath would do you a lot more good than that old onion."

"No fears it would," he says, "I give up bathing years ago when I found out I had to use water."

'Course, his missus makes him worse y'know. I mind she said to him one time she said "Ha!" she says, "you ain't having no bath," she says, "you stay smelly – that way, if you wus to get lost, I won't have no trouble finding you!"

"No," says old Hener, "I don't expect you would – but if *you* wus to get lost, I wouldn't have no trouble!"

'Course, his missus has been like that ever since Hener tripped one time when he wus h'emptying Miss Peacock's sanitorium bucket, and spilled some of it down his trousers.

"Hello!" she bellows, when he got home, "been hanging round Miss Peacock again have we? No need to deny it," she says, "I can smell the perfume!"

'Course, that wus all because of onions and garlic and h'outdoor sanitorium buckets, as to why him and her never started a family afore they did. Well, he smelled that bad, his missus reckoned she couldn't never get close enough, never mind for long enough, to start one!

I don't reckon they would've had any young 'uns at all, if old Hener hadn't a'joined the Home Guard – and got issued with one of them there gas-masks!

I mind she told the Women's Institute some time afterwards – well, they tell each other everything don't they – that in six years of being married to old Hener, she ain't never managed once to get within four foot of him – and of course, if you wants to start a family, well – four foot ain't quite close enough is it!*

But the minute he bought that old gas-mask home – and his missus tried it out on him – well, there weren't no holding her back! She got close enough then alright, and d'you know, their first one wus born exactly nine months to the very day when that old gas-mask wus took into that house!

She had nine more after that y'know, in no time at all – and she only stopped having 'em then on account as the war ended, and old Hener had to take the gas-mask back!

She reckoned as how that wus the bestest invention since vacuated milk!

Ha, every time she took that gas-mask from off the nail on the back of the kitchen door, old Hener knowed what she wus after! She wanted to hang on to it y'know, but old Hener wouldn't hear of it.

"No fear!" he says, "I reckon ten childs is enough for anybody – if there's any more left in that old gas-mask," he says, "we'll let some other beggar have 'em!" So he wrapped it up in a copy of The Family Planning Weekly, and handed it back to the Home Guard Captain, old Dr Simmons.

You just think y'know, if that hadn't a'been for that old gas-mask – why, that marriage might never have been consumed!

That weren't very long after that, when Dr Simmons had a visit from Mary Feathers the Dung Carter's wife. She'd got the same complaint as old Hener's missus y'know – fourfootitis! She'd tried to get rid of it with all the usual cure-alls – like disinfectant, penetrating oil, and swearing – but of course, none of them worked.

When she told the old Doctor what her trouble wus, he just smiled, and handed her the gas-mask, still wrapped up in The Family Planning Weekly – just as old Hener had give it to him.

"Here you are," he says, "put this on every night just before you go to bed – that'll do the trick.'

"Oh!" says Mary, "that's nice, d'you think it'll work then?"

"Well," says the old Doctor, "that worked overtime for Mrs Padfield, and I reckon her Hener smells twice as bad as your Harry."

"Ah well," she says, taking the gas-mask out of the box, "I'd better see if it fits then," and starts undoing her stays!

"No, no!" shouted the old Doctor, a'wincing at the size of Mary Feathers, "it

*At this point in the monologue, during a performance in an Old Tyme Music Hall taking place at the Elgiva Hall, Chesham, the Master of Ceremonies shouted – "You speak for yourself mate!" . . . needless to say – it brought the house down! From then on, it was included in every subsequent performance!

don't go there – don't take 'em off! *don't take 'em off!* – we shan't never get 'em back on again!"

"Now come on Doctor," says Mary, not taking a blind bit of notice of what he wus a'saying, "I've got to try it on ain't I?"

"Just a minute then!" says Dr Simmons, reaching for the medicine cabinet. "Just a minute! If you're taking them fearful old stays off, I must insist on an anaesthetic!"

"Anaesthetic?" says Mary, "I don't want no anaesthetic!"

" 'Course you don't," says the old Doctor – taking a wonderful swig from out of a whisky bottle, "that ain't for you!"

"Oh dear," says Mary, struggling to get the gas-mask over her thighs, "that won't go up no further – d'you reckon you could give us a hand to undo the strap a bit more?"

"No fear!" says Dr Simmons, taking another swig out of the bottle, "I ain't getting no closer!"

"Why ever not?" says Mary, "you're a Doctor ain't you?"

"Yes," he says, "that's why I ain't getting no closer – I wants to stay one! Besides," he says, "I hate suffering."

"What d'you mean?" says Mary, "I ain't suffering!"

So he says "No," he says, "but if you undoes any more notches on them there stays – I shall be!"

"Well!" says Mary, taking the gas-mask off her legs, "for all the good that's going to do me, I might as well put it over me head!"

"Thank goodness for that!" says the old Doctor, "at last we're getting somewhere!"

So in the end, that's what she did.

"Now then," says the old Doctor, "now you've got it on – you smell!"

"*You what?*" says Mary.

"You smell, you smell!" says the old Doctor, and before he realised what he'd said, an empty gas-mask box walloped him one round the earhole!

"Ooooh!" bellows the old Doctor – "no, no, no – you just smell with the gas-mask on!"

Well, that wus a lucky job he wus born with two earholes, because if he hadn't have been, I dread to think where the gas-mask box would've landed that time.

"Oh dear, oh dear!" says Dr Simmons, "for goodness sake give me that blessed gas-mask and let me show you how it works – there," he says as he put it on, "then you takes a deep sniff – and that takes away all the nasty smells."

"How do you know?" says Mary, "there ain't none in here."

"Oh, I don't know," says the old Doctor, as he rang the bell for the next customer to come in – "you'd be surprised at some of the horrible smells what finds their way in here!"

Well, d'you know, he wus just a'saying that, when who should walk in through the door but old Miss Peacock! 'Course, she couldn't be off but see the old Doctor wearing the gas-mask – but when she heard what he said! Well – that done it!

I shan't try to tell you what happened next, 'cause I reckon that would take all night – but old Doctor Simmons – well – he took the rest of the day off, and staggered home clutching his whisky bottle – while at the same time, trying to hold everything what hurt!

Mary Feathers – well – she went home with the gas-mask and had six childs – eventually!

. . . And Miss Peacock? Well, she just went home – empty handed! Well, it ain't no good going home with a recipe, is it, if you ain't got the main ingredient when you get there?!

Y'know – that's wonderful what you can get out of a gas-mask ain't it, and by the way – if you knows of anybody as wants one, they do tell me that old Doctor Simmons as got hundreds of them stacked in his garden shed just waiting to be collected! – but he'll always insist on showing you how to use them first . . .

. . . and you can't really blame him for that now can you!

Brusher Morley's story continues on page 108

~12~ You need more than a Bag of Clubs when you've got Six-and-a-half Thousand Golf Balls...

MATCH PLAY, Stapleford, Medal Play – all this meant absolutely nothing to Albert Medders when he first started his Greenkeeper's Apprenticeship up at the Golf Club.

He knowed all about tees and caddies, of course, on account his old Mum kept a café up in the village. He probably knowed more about them than what the Head Greenkeeper did, and of course, he knowed all there was to know about scratch, because when he was at school, that was all he ever did – until the old Nit Nurse comed round and shaved all his hair off, like she did to most of us! Ha! And not just off your head neither! That was all Horace's fault of course – but I'll explain more about him in a minute or two.

Nurse Lyle – that was her name. Hor, she was a devil she was! – took great delight in pushing her fingers through your hair just as hard as ever she could in her never ending search for fleas, and if she found any, then woe betide you, because off comed all your clothes and the search continued elsewhere! And as if that weren't bad enough, when you got home and told your Mum, they all had to come off again, and she began a systematic search through everything you'd got on with a fine tooth-comb – and that went on for another fortnight, or at least, until your old Mum was satisfied she'd got rid of them all!

Good old boy is Albert y'know – been Assistant to the Head Greenkeeper up at the Golf Club for a few years now – clean, tidy, and very good at his job too. Ha, the Head Greenkeeper has made a good job out of Albert, really licked him into shape so to speak – a bit different from when he was at school, and that's a fact! He was – well, just cast your mind back to your own school days, there was always one in your class weren't there – a snotty-nosed kid, with socks halfway down to his ankles, and shoes caked in half a fieldful of mud! In our class that kid was Albert Medders, and y'know, he'd always got a great lambstail a'hanging from the end of his nose! Some kids always did have didn't they.

He was well liked at school though was Albert. There was only one thing – he was always covered in fleas! – which was hardly surprising really. Well y'see, his old Dad kept a few chickens out the back, and that was Albert's job to feed them every morning before he comed to school. Hor, and they was the most flea-ridden bunch of fowls you'd ever come across. It's no wonder he was always scratching, because he used to sit on the perch alongside 'em and stroke em – especially one big old cockerel called Horace. He was absolutely alive with them. Now Horace thought the world of Albert, and followed him to school most mornings. When Albert went into class, Horace would fly up to the open window, jump onto Albert's desk, flap his wings like billyho and let out an almighty crow – y'know – like all good cockerels do!

Well, if you never had fleas when you started off to school, you certainly got 'em after you arrived, because when old Horace flapped his wings, a huge great cloud of them flew into the air, then descended on every kid in the class – so of course, when the old Nit Nurse comed round for her monthly inspection, that was always our class she comed to first! And poor old Albert was the first one to be dragged out by the earholes for inspection.

Ha! them's were the days . . . but where was I? Oh yes – I remember . . . up at the Golf Club!

So anyway, whilst Albert was attending his interview in the clubhouse, the old Vicar and Percy Lamkin were getting themselves ready to spread the Gospel. Ever since Miss Arkley's old mattress had saved the Vicar from serious injury, he'd decided to pin as many of his notices saying:

ANYONE WHO CALLS UPON THE NAME OF THE LORD,
SHALL BE SAVED!

on as many notice-boards as possible, to help him spread the good news as far afield as he could.

Tomorrow it was the turn of the Golf Club. Percy was in the Vicar's garden shed getting things prepared, and busily sawing, when in walked the old Vicar just in time to see six foot drop off the end of his bestest ladder.

"Hey, hey, hey!" shouted the old Vicar, "what on earth are you doing Lamkin – that's my bestest ladder that is."

"Wouldn't fit me barrer nicely," says Percy, "but it does now."

"Wouldn't fit your barrer, wouldn't fit your barrer?" says the old Vicar. "I don't suppose it occurred to you that now you've sawn six foot off the end, it won't reach the top of the Golf Club notice-board."

"Reach it? Reach it?" says old Percy, " 'Course the beggar will reach it – d'you think I'm stupid? I sawed it off the bottom – not the top!"

"Well, bless me," says the old Vicar, "that's clever – I never thought of that."

"Ha!" says Percy, feeling quite pleased that he'd got one over on the old Vicar, "I ain't as daft as you look y'know."

Back in the clubhouse, Albert was in the middle of his interview with the Head Greenkeeper.

"Right then, Albert," says the Head Greenkeeper, "let's see how much you know about golf – do you know the names of any clubs?"

. . . Now, before Albert left home for his interview by the Head Greenkeeper for the job as his Assistant, his old Dad took him to one side and told him a few home truths.

"Now listen, Albert," he said "and listen good! I hear say there's been quite a response after this job up at the Golf Course, most of 'em from college boys – chaps who have had a far better education than you have. Now, you ain't going to get the job by trying to be clever. That just ain't going to work – you're going to have to use your brains, so if you've really got your heart set on the job – then this is what you'll have to do . . ."

"Well," says Albert, in answer to the question, "there's the Dart's Club, the Young Farmers' Club, and then there's the Women's Institute . . . "

"No, no, no!" says the Head Greenkeeper, "not them sort of clubs – I meant golf clubs! We'll skip that for now, and go on to the next question – what do you know about Albatrosses and Eagles?"

. . . Now when that comed to a bit of bird-watching, Albert was your man. Knowed all about them he did. Why, he'd seen dozens of Albatrosses and Eagles flying over Hawridge Common woods only the other day . . .

"Why," says Albert, "them's birdies."

"No they ain't," says the Head Greenkeeper, "birdies are the ones you get under par."

"Not the ones that I've seen," replied Albert, "they're the ones you get over Hawridge Common Woods."

"Never mind that!" says the Head Greenkeeper, "d'you know . . ." – and he was just in the middle of saying – "d'you know what a bogey is?" when Albert gave an almighty sniff – and a blessed great lambstail what had been a'dangling from the end of his nose disappeared – just like that there!

"You needn't bother to answer that question!" sighed the Head Greenkeeper. "Ughhhh – for goodness sake – ain't you got a blessed handkerchief?"

"Why?" sniffed Albert, "d'you want one then?"

"No I don't," shouted the Head Greenkeeper. "Now then, I shall ask you one more question – and this time, you'd better get it right or else . . . *d'you know what a wood is?*"

" 'Course I do," says Albert, "it's that group of trees over at Hawridge Common what I was telling you about – y'know, where all them Albatrosses and Eagles fly!"

. . . It was then that the Head Greenkeeper's attitude changed. He looked at the snotty-nosed lad of 15 years and a bit standing before him – still in short trousers, because that was all his Mum could afford – socks halfway down to his ankles, and his shoes still caked in mud from out of his Dad's chicken run – and his mind went back to the other applicants for the job of Assistant Greenkeeper – all of them, it must be said, very smart young men. What a difference, he thought, between them and young Albert here, although he did notice he'd made an effort to tidy himself up a bit by wiping his shoes on the back of his socks – y'know, like we all did when we were at school!

But there was something about Albert that endeared him to himself. He glanced at the young lad again – and at that precise moment, he knew he had found his man. He wondered why he hadn't noticed it before, but then realised his gaze had been transfixed for most of the interview, on the lambstail a'dangling from the end of Albert's nose. But when he looked into his eyes, he saw what he was looking for. It had been there all the time – how could he have missed that sparkle of honesty – the intensity – the anticipation – not to mention the anxiety . . . and his heart went out to him!

He spoke at last, in a quiet, controlled voice . . .

"That's the wrong answer, Albert, wrong, wrong, wrong – in fact," he said, "your answers to all the questions were wrong – but d'you know what," he says, "I don't mind, I don't mind at all. I've interviewed dozens of chaps for this particular job, and every last one of them has come here waving their diploma papers about, and making out they know more about the job than I do. Next thing you know, they'll be after my job, and I can't be having that – so Albert me boy, you're just the chap I'm a'looking for, and I'm pleased to say you've got the job – because at the end of the day I want somebody that I can teach, not somebody who wants to teach me . . . "

"Good old Dad," said Albert to himself, "you got it right as usual – that's *exactly* what you said he would say!"

" . . . Just one more thing before we go outside," says the Head Greenkeeper, "d'you know what a handicap is?"

"Someone who walks with a limp?" volunteered Albert.

"I like a challenge," says the Head Greenkeeper, "we've got a few scratch golfers up here . . . "

"They didn't go to the same school as I did then," says Albert, "because old Nurse Lyle would've soon sorted them out!"

" . . . but most of them," he says, completely ignoring Albert's remark, "have got a handicap . . . "

"I can't see anybody outside walking with a limp," says Albert, peering through the clubhouse window.

". . . and now," says the Head Greenkeeper, grabbing Albert and leading him out of the clubhouse by the earhole – "*I've got one too!*"

When they got outside, the Head Greenkeeper suddenly stopped.

"Just one more question Albert," he says, and he lowered his voice so nobody else could hear, "tell me – have you *really* seen Albatrosses and Eagles over Hawridge Common . . . ?"

Albert then, at the start of his career, was feeling very pleased at the way his interview turned out. As far as he was concerned, life was looking particularly good.

Up at Charley Buckley's Windmill, however, which stands adjacent to the 16th hole of the golf course, the situation wasn't quite as rosy. His flock of free range chickens were being continually peppered by badly struck golf balls, causing him all sorts of problems. All his protests to the Golf Club fell on deaf ears, and so, instead of chucking the wayward balls back over the fence like he used to when it first started, he decided to hang on to them. He stacks 'em all in wheelbarrows y'know – a thousand at a time!

At the last count – he had six-and-a-half barrowfuls parked up in his shed! He would've had a lot more than that, only his old Missus, being a bit short-sighted an' that, sold 15 dozen of 'em on her egg round! Old Charley reckoned it out, that given the going rate of sixpence a time for second-hand golf balls, he stood to make far more out of them than he ever did by selling fresh eggs at the farm gate.

Old Miss Peacock bought some of the ones that Charley's missus sold y'know, and that weren't very long before she comed storming up to the Windmill demanding her money back!

"About them blessed eggs of yours Buckley," she says, "went to pick them up, and the bottom of the paper bag fell out, but instead of smashing to pieces, they bounced about five foot in the air and rolled off down the hill!"

"I see," says Charley, "and I suppose you want some more to replace 'em then?"

"No, that I don't," she says, "the way they bounce and roll I reckon you'll be better off trying to sell 'em as golf balls!"

But when the Golf Club found out how many balls he'd collected, they reckoned as how that was stealing, and demanded them all back.

Charley said they could have 'em back just as soon as they resolved the situation, by re-aligning the 16th hole away from his chickens – or when *he* was good and ready! And, according to the village grapevine, that time was fast approaching as he was getting a bit short on wheelbarrows!

Little did the Golf Club realise, however, that the time for the return of their prodigal golf balls was imminent – but never in a million years would they have envisaged the method of such a return. But when it eventually happened – they had only themselves to blame.

If only they had studied their geographical location more carefully . . . !

After dinner, as Charley Buckley donned his hard hat and dodged yet more flying golf balls on his way down to feed the chickens, and collect a few eggs, he was thinking about those six-and-a-half thousand golf balls taking up all that valuable wheelbarrow space. How could he return them without appearing to lose face as it were and, at the same time, teach the Golf Club a lesson for all the aggravation they had caused him over the last few months? How could he . . . ?

. . . "*Fore!*" came the cry from the golf course, and his train of thought was savagely shattered as an errant golf ball crashed its way through the trees, and struck his hard hat the most *almightiest* of blows . . . *clunk!* that went. It ricocheted off at a tremendous speed – miles in the air it went, over the tree-tops and disappeared from sight!

What happened next was just as if a door had been flung open in his mind!

"*That's it!*" he hollered, "*that's it – that's exactly the way to do it!*" and he felt just like Percy Lamkin felt that time, when his emotions got the better of him – y'know, when he got the job as Miss Arkley's part-time handyman . . . and so Charley did a Percy – and danced a jig in the middle of his chicken pen!

"*Yes – yes – yes!*" he shouted at the top of his voice, "*you need more than a driver when you've got six-and-a-half thousand golf balls!*"

When he arrived back at the Windmill, he found the Golf Club had left a message for him . . . with regard to the three trampolines that you are storing for us. Would you kindly deliver them to the rear of the clubhouse as soon as possible, as they are required for the Golf Club Open Day – *and don't forget our golf balls* . . . !

"Blessed cheek they got," says Charley, "all the aggravation they are causing, and now they ask me to deliver their flippin' tamborines – I've a good mind not . . . *just a minute – just a minute* . . . !" and suddenly, he burst out laughing, not ordinary laughter you understand, more like uncontrollable laughter. He laughed and laughed so much that his sides ached, and the tears rolled down his cheeks . . .

"*Ha! Ha! Ha! Ha! Ha!*" he chortled, "I can see it all – this is getting better by the minute!"

Unfortunately for Albert, Nurse Lyle and a few of her fellow players arrived at the 16th tee, just as he was bending down doing some repair work.

"I must be seeing things," she says, "because if I'm not very much mistaken, that head of hair belongs to *none other than Albert Medders!* I'd recognise that flea-ridden mop anywhere!

"Medders," she bellers, "come over here – what do you think you're doing on our golf course?"

As Albert drew near, she eyed him up and down, but couldn't believe what she was seeing. Gone was the snotty nose, gone were the short trousers, and in the place of the shoes that were always caked with half a fieldful of mud, he had on a nice new shiny pair of boots.

"I work here, Miss." says Albert.

"Not with a head of hair like that you're not," she says, "we don't tolerate folkses with fleas on our golf course." And before Albert had a chance to protest, she was pushing her old fingers through his hair as hard as ever she could, in a determined effort to find a few fleas – much to the amusement of her golfing cronies. She searched frantically, but she couldn't find neary one at all!

"No, and you won't neither," said a voice behind her, almost making her jump out of her skin, "you ought to be ashamed of yourself – now leave the lad alone," said the Head Greenkeeper (for it was he who's voice it was), "you get on with your golf, and let him get on with his work!"

Albert and the Head Greenkeeper stood back on the edge of the tee as Nurse Lyle – still smarting from the dressing down she had received in front of her cronies, furiously addressed her teed-up golf ball.

She was half-way down her backswing when Albert sniffed and casually remarked "Looks like another one for Charley Buckley's chicken pen!"

He received a severe rollicking from Nurse Lyle, and a yellow card from the Head

Greenkeeper for that remark, who went on to explain that the rules of golf etiquette clearly state that no-one shall breathe, speak, blink, scratch, sniff or generally move about when anyone is about to play a stroke.

Albert apologised to Nurse Lyle when eventually she managed to get one to stay on the fairway, and promised he'd call into Charley Buckley's on his way home, and ask for her other four balls back!

Albert and the Head Greenkeeper started on their way back to the workshop at the rear of the clubhouse as Nurse Lyle and her fellow players hacked their way down the 16th fairway.

"Come on Albert," said the Head Greenkeeper, "I can't bear to watch – look at all that lovely turf flying through the air – never ought to be allowed near a golf course did some folks!"

They were just going to put the kettle on for a cup of tea, when Charley Buckley turned up with his horse and cart, delivering the Golf Club's three huge great trampolines.

"Blimey!" says the Head Greenkeeper, "I'd forgotten all about the Golf Club Open Day – we'll have 'em over here mate," he says to old Charley, "we'll line 'em all up behind the clubhouse."

"My pleasure!" says old Charley, with the sort of glint in his eye that tells you he was up to summat. "Just here?" he asked, "or maybe perhaps a bit further back, away from that wall a bit more? Don't want the kiddies hurting themselves now do we!"

Of course, Albert had to have a go didn't he – because when that comed to a bit of trampolining, just like bird-watching, Albert was your man! Off comed his new boots, and he clambered on. You should've seen him go – miles up in the air he went – down he come again – miles up in the air he went – down he come again – miles up in the air . . .

"What can you see from up there?" says the Head Greenkeeper.

"Charley Buckley's Windmill," says Albert, "plus a few Eagles and several Albatrosses!" and he ducked just in time on the way down, as one of his nice new shiny boots flashed past his earhole – but unfortunately, he caught the other one on the way up – ar – right where it hurts most!

Charley Buckley smiled to himself as he watched young Albert bouncing up and down on the trampoline – apparently none the worse for wear. Things were turning out far better than he could ever have wished for . . . as far as he was concerned, tomorrow couldn't arrive quickly enough!

As he was walking home across the golf course that evening, Albert was deep in thought about his first day's work in his new job, and Nurse Lyle. He was thinking as how he would like to get his own back on her, for the way she humiliated him on the 16th tee, in front of her fellow golfers.

"But how?" he said to himself. "What chance have I got of doing that?"

He was just approaching the stile that led the way to Charley Buckley's Windmill, when he spotted something lying on the ground ahead of him.

"Hello," he says. "Looks like someone's lost their hat – just a minute, that's Nurse Lyle's old woolly hat I know – that must have dropped off her golf bag – ah well, I'll take it home and give it to the old so-and-so in the morning."

He still couldn't think of a way to get his own back on Nurse Lyle y'know – try as he might – until he went down the garden later that evening to shut his Dad's chickens in for the night. He saw Horace stood on his perch having a good old scratch – y'know, like all good cockerels do, and that comed to him in a flash – just like that there!

"*Got it!*" he shouted. "*Yes! Got it!*" He pulled Nurse Lyle's woolly hat from out of his pocket, looked at old Horace – then at the woolly hat – and promptly laid it on the perch right next to the old flea-laden cockerel!

"That should do it," he says, "and tomorrow, I'll slip it in her golf bag, and she won't even realise she lost it at all!"

In the early hours of the next morning, just as that was getting peek o'daylight, Albert heard Horace flap his wings and give a few lusty crows – as all good cockerels do at that time of the morning!

"Lovely!" says Albert to himself as he lay in bed, "that old woolly hat should be well alive be now!" and he turned over and went back to sleep for a couple of hours!

Half a mile separated the Windmill from the golf course – a very steep, very straight half a mile. The only way to reach the Golf Club by road, was by turning left at the Windmill, then straight down the hill to the clubhouse which lay right at the bottom. It had always been a rough, unmade road – full of potholes and stones – but all that changed when the Golf Club took up residence; in come the Council and completely transformed it into a beautifully smooth luxurious roadway – for the exclusive use of the Golf Club!

They even installed a traffic calming thing-a-me-jig – what we used to call a Sleeping Policeman – about 10 yards from the bottom of the hill, right in front of the clubhouse.

Charley Buckley stood on the top floor of the Windmill, surveying the golf course that lay below him half a mile away, then took out his ready reckoner to check that his figures – the ones that he had worked out earlier in the day – were indeed correct.

"Perfect," he says, "just absolutely blooming perfect!"

Albert crept away from the ladies locker room early the next morning, after successfully returning Nurse Lyle's flea-laden woolly hat to her golf bag and trolly undetected.

The old Vicar and Percy Lamkin arrived shortly afterwards, armed with all sorts of goodies loaded on Percy's wheelbarrow – stacks of leaflets to pin up all round the course, loads of hymn books for a good old sing-song in the clubhouse after the match and, last but not least, the Vicar's newly shortened version of his bestest ladder!

Today was Ladies Day – with one of the most prestigious prizes of the year at stake – The Ladies Captain's Silver Medal!

Everybody was turning up now, all ready for an early start to their golfing day. Nurse Lyle and her golfing cronies were among the first of them – and she never gave her woolly hat a second glance! Young Albert was right y'know, she'd never even missed it!

The golf match was well under way with the players spread well out all over the course.

Nurse Lyle was already in hot water with her playing companions, being accused of gamesmanship and bad sporting behaviour due to her incessant scratching and irritating sudden movements. It proved too much for her partners, and when they all gathered closely around her eyeball to eyeball – to lodge their protests even more vigorously – well, you know what fleas do best don't you, besides biting of course, the little beggars jump don't they – and Horace's little beggars were no exception!

Before long, all four were at it – scratching, jumping, and generally making themselves a blessed nuisance to all the other golfers out on the course. So much so, in fact, that the Ladies Captain comed over and told them in no uncertain terms that their unsportsman-like actions could no longer be tolerated – and they were asked to leave the course there and then . . .

. . . and a disguised voice from behind a hillock some distance away shouted: "*And take your fleas with you!*"

The old Vicar and Percy Lamkin were busy at the main notice-board immediately behind the clubhouse, just down from the trampolines.

The Vicar was on the top rung of his much shortened ladder – standing on tiptoe as usual – berating Percy in no uncertain terms over the ladder being too blessed short, and how it was all his fault – struggling to pin up the first notice on the board. It was the usual one, y'know:

ANYONE WHO CALLS UPON THE NAME OF THE LORD, SHALL BE SAVED!

Charley Buckley, in the meantime, was busy wheeling out his six-and-a-half wheelbarrows of golf balls and lining them all up at the top of the hill, ready for their return to the rightful owners. He tipped another 100 balls into the half-filled wheelbarrow – just to make the speech he was going to do in a minute or so – absolutely correct!

Albert had returned to the workshop along with the Head Greenkeeper, and whilst waiting for the kettle to boil, decided to have a go on the trampolines.

Up and down he went, gathering height at every jump, until at last he could see the Windmill, and Charley Buckley – with all his wheelbarrows lined up at the top of the hill! He could tell in an instant exactly what it was that Charley was up to!

He hollered out to the Head Greenkeeper, who promptly jumped onto one of the other trampolines – he knew how to do it because he'd had plenty of practice watching young Albert, but when he arrived at the top of the jump, and saw for himself what was going on, he shouted to everyone in earshot – and being an ex-naval man he knew exactly what to say . . . !

"Abandon ship! Abandon ship! We are under attack! About to be torpedoed by six-and-a-half thousand golf balls! Abandon ship! Abandon ship! Every man for himself!" and he and Albert scrambled off the trampolines as fast as ever they could and took refuge in their toolshed!

For Charley Buckley this was war! And for war, you had to be dressed in the proper manner. He'd rooted out his old Home Guard uniform, bedecked with its three stripes and medals, together with his highly polished boots complete with gaiters. He looked every last inch of him a fighting man – resplendant, determined and, in the eyes of his missus, heroic, because he was fighting for what he believed to be right, and if this was the only way to get the Golf Club to see reason – then so be it!

Charley Buckley stood behind his Golf Ball Launchers, picked up his megaphone, and hollered . . .

"*Now hear this Golf Club – now hear this – the mass return of all your golf balls is imminent . . . !*"

. . . And the noise it created was deafening! – and the instructions reverberated throughout the surrounding villages for miles around!

. . . "*Prepare to defend yourselves – you've got ten minutes to batten down the hatches, board up your windows, do whatever else you have to do . . . then take cover!*"

. . . "*Nine minutes 40 seconds and counting!*" bawled Charley.

Well, you never see'd anything like it in all your born days. They all comed tearing out of the clubhouse, boarded up the windows and teared back inside again.

Everybody in the vicinity and the surrounding area of the clubhouse dived for cover. They holed up in the bunkers, took cover behind the trees, and hid behind

all the hillocks, just peeping over the tops to see what was going on – and they were not a second too soon . . . everyone had taken cover – everyone that is apart from the old Vicar! He was still stood standing on tip-toe at the top of his ladder, completely oblivious of the pandemonium that was taking place all over the golf course. Percy Lamkin had tried shouting up to him, but it was no good! He was singing as he climbed the ladder, Number 545 from the Church Hymninal (he had to change one of the words a bit just to make it sound authentic, but he was sure the Good Lord wouldn't mind just the one. . . !)

"*. . . nearer my God to thee, nearer to thee,*
E'en though it be a ladder (should've been Cross)
That raiseth me;
Still all my song shall be,
Nearer, my God, to thee,
Nearer to thee . . ."

He continued climbing ever upward, through the second verse, and carried on climbing – it really was a huge great notice-board – and the nearer he got to the top of course, the louder he sang,

Then he started the third verse . . .

"*. . . There let the way appear*
steps unto heaven . . . "

and then, not changing the tune at all he sang . . .

"*. . . Except that we are six rungs short Lord*
because Lamkin sawed the beggars off . . . !

In the end, Percy gave up the shouting as a bad job – and joined Albert and the Head Greenkeeper in the toolshed!

Up the other side of the valley, attracted by all the noise and kerfuffle, hundreds and hundreds of villagers, who had rushed to the scene, were now standing ten deep at either side of the Golf Club road staring wide-eyed at Charley Buckley – majestic in all his Home Guard regalia. They soon cottoned on as to what was happening, of course, and they all joined in Charley's countdown with a fervour bordering on patriotism – it was the uniform that did it! – that, and the Englishman's renowned support for the little man against the big bad barons. A modern day David versus Goliath this was – and they had all turned up to support their very own David!

But whatever else Charley Buckley was, he was nobody's fool. He wasn't out to hurt anyone – he'd never hurt a soul in his life! If folkses were still scrabbling for cover, he would've delayed the countdown. He saw the old Vicar perched on his abridged ladder, but, if his calculations proved correct, he would be perfectly safe . . . just! Everybody else had taken cover . . .

. . . "3 . . . 2 . . . 1 . . . *Fire!*" went up the roar from the vast gallery of onlookers – then stood with baited breath whilst Charley's own countdown caught up.

. . . "3 . . . 2 . . . 1 . . . *Fire!*" shouted Charley – and tipped up the half-filled, and a bit more, wheelbarrow!

"*Charge!*" roared Charley, as the first 600 golf balls careered down the hill at breakneck speed . . .

"*. . . Into the valley of golf rolled the 600 . . . !*"

They must have been travelling at 100 miles an hour when they hit the Sleeping Policeman at the foot of the hill. The result was as stupendous as it was spectacular! They took off like machine-gun bullets – all in lightning succession. They shot over the roof of the clubhouse, and every last one of them landed right in the middle of the trio of trampolines.

If Charley Buckley thought the leap from the Sleeping Policeman was brilliant, goodness knows what he thought of the next one! They hit the trampolines full bore, then went hurtling miles into space cavorting in all directions over the entire bottom half of the golf course.

The cheering from the Windmill side was absolutely deafening! The "Oooooohs" and the "Aaaaaahs" echoed and re-echoed all over the golf course.

The old Vicar – still at the top of his ladder – was singing the first part of verse five – and in a world of his own. . . !

"*. . . Or, if on a joyful wing*
Cleaving the sky,
Sun, moon, and stars forgot,
Upwards I fly"

. . . just as the first fusillade of golf balls cleaving the sky like guided missiles, flew upwards towards him. He turned as the sudden noise of golf balls hitting trampoline penetrated his ears above the singing, and saw to his horror, that he was in direct line of fire, and yet again, faced with mortal danger, he called upon the name of the Lord in his hour of need . . .

". . . *Oh, Good Lord*" he shouted –

"*Save me – save me!*" . . .

. . . and d'you know – every one of the 600 balls passed about a foot over his head – just as Charley Buckley had calculated! He scrabbled down the ladder, a lot faster than he went up I can tell you, and went rushing over to the toolshed!

"*Did you see that Lamkin?*" he shouted, "*Did you see that? All them there golf balls?*"

"Yes," says Percy, "we saw 'em all, didn't we chaps?"

"We did an' all," says the Head Greenkeeper, "they only just missed you Vicar."

"But not by much," says Albert.

"But don't – don't you see Lamkin," says the old Vicar, "the Good Lord has once again saved me from serious injury!"

"How d'you make that out?" says Percy, "I didn't see him on top of the ladder."

"You still don't see? If you hadn't sawed six foot off my bestest ladder yesterday, I would have been struck by every one of them there golf balls. The Good Lord has saved me yet again," and he went rushing outside to spread the good news, just as the next barrowful of balls hit the Sleeping Policeman full tilt. Up, up they soared – down, down they dropped – right on target with unerring accuracy once again exploding off the trampolines, speeding to every corner, tee, fairway, bunker and green on the lower reaches of the golf course!

The bombardment continued for half an hour or so, with every spectator lining the hill from top to bottom, cheering wildly as each wheelbarrowful of balls were launched on their special mission – and not until the final ball had come to rest, did Charley Buckley pause to mop his brow. He surveyed the scene below. It was, indeed, a truly awsome sight. A sea of white covered the entire lower reaches of the golf course – just like snow – except of course, it was in the middle of July!

Spontaneous applause broke out amongst the folks on the hill – what a spectacle they had all witnessed, and the cheering continued for a full two minutes. Charley said afterwards, he felt just like the British Open Champion must feel, when he walks towards the 18th green on the final day of the Championship.

But it was impossible for him to contain his delight at the outstanding success of his bombardment. Never in all his wildest dreams could he have wished for a better outcome.

He danced another jig just as Percy Lamkin did, and he hollered out at the top of his voice – through his megaphone. . . .

". . . *Who needs a bagful of golf clubs*
when I've got a Sleeping Policeman . . ."

– then, really rubbing salt into the wound –

". . . *and you've got three tambourines!* . . ."

His laughter echoed all over the golf course and the surrounding area . . .

. . . "*Ha, ha, ha, ha, ha, ha!*" he chortled in an uncontrollable outburst – "*ha, ha, ha, ha, ha, ha!*"

Down at the Golf Club, everybody slowly emerged from wherever it was they had taken refuge from the severe onslaught and surveyed the awe-inspiring scene around them. Golf balls were everywhere – as far as the eye could see. Every nook and every cranny, and every hole on every green throughout the entire lower reaches of the course was filled to overflowing . . . !

. . . and everybody there agreed that they had never, in all their years of golfing, seen so many holes in one – so many Eagles – or so many Albatrosses – scored on the same golf course – in the same match – all on the same day!

. . . and they also agreed, down to the very last one of them, that the first prize at stake in the Golf Match today – The Ladies Captain's Silver Medal – should be awarded to none other than Charley Buckley himself, for the best round of golf ever witnessed at their Golf Club.

Then they all turned to face the Windmill in salute to the man who had not only returned all their golf balls, but the manner in which he had done so, without injury to a single one of them – an ingenious and well engineered plan of campaign.

Someone started clapping, others joined in, and before long the whole course erupted into a cacophony of clapping and cheering – and all the villagers on the Windmill hillside, joined in once again with the spontaneous applause. It was a never to be forgotten scene – the likes of which has never been equalled on any golf course in the whole of England!

Later that same evening, as Charley donned his hard hat once again, he pondered to himself if the Golf Club would ever resolve the situation.

"Time alone will tell," he mused to himself. "Ah well, I wonder how many we've got today?" – and as he counted the balls into his bucket, yet another one was cracked down the fairway.

"One – two – three – now let's see, what comes after three?" . . . "*Fore!*" came the answer from the 16th tee . . . "Oh yes – thanks mate," says Charley, "five – six – seven . . . "

~13~
Unlucky for Some...

HAVE YOU EVER noticed, as you travel along life's highway, how many events seem to occur in threes? For instance, the churchyard gates seldom open for just the one, do they, and a preacher's sermon on a Sunday is nearly always delivered in three parts, ain't it?

We had a visiting preacher up at the church a while back y'know. One dark, cold November Sunday it were. Comed all the way from Wendover on his bike. That's foreign parts is Wendover y'know – and uphill best part of the way! Me and Billy Puddick wus already in church when he arrived and d'you know, he wus that cold and so much out of breath after biking all that way, that Billy, in his capacity as Sexton and Verger, asked him if he would care for a stiff whisky and soda – y'know, just to warm him up a bit, to act as a kind of reviver like.

"Well," he says, "I didn't ought to really Mr Puddick," he says, "but yes, on this occasion, I think perhaps I might be tempted – and I'll give you three very good reasons as to why. Firstly, I definitely feel the need for some – what shall I say? – some warming liquid refreshment such as would sustain a very cold mortal, after a strenuous cycle ride all the way from Wendover. Secondly, a little bit of Dutch courage certainly wouldn't go amiss to help with the deliverance of my sermon a little later on, and thirdly . . . " But before he had the chance to say any more, Miss Peacock, who had been lurking nearby, put in her twopennyworth . . .

. . . "There is no thirdly," she bellered, as she grabbed the whisky tumbler out of Billy Puddick's hand, "no preacher drinks alcoholic licquor in my church – 'specially one who ought to be a member of our Temperance Society." And in one gulp, she removed the temptation.

"Ah me," sighed the preacher all the way from Wendover, as he resigned himself to the fact that he weren't going to get any warming alcoholic sustenance on this particular Sunday morning, "that's what we in the trade calls divine intervention." So in the end, he settled for a nice cup of tea instead.

A few days after that, me, Billy and Percy Lamkin had a job to do in the churchyard, only Percy hadn't turned up, so we went on without him. A gloomy old day it were – shrouded in thick mist and fog. When we got along there with our wheelbarrers, we found that Miss Peacock had parked her pony and trap right across the gateway, and we couldn't get in, so old Billy asked her – quite politely for him I might add – if she would mind moving along a bit so's we could get through with our barrers.

"No, that I'm not!" she says, and then, remembering about the preacher from Wendover she says, "and I'll give you three good reasons why I'm not."

"Firstly," she says, "I'm here on official, important Parish business – which is more than you two are. Secondly," she says, "I wus here before the both of you, so you can just get lost! . . . And thirdly . . . "

"There ain't no thirdly, Miss," interrupted old Billy, "because we're here on even more important Parish business." And then, peering through the mist as though he were looking for summat to appear, he said, very solemnly, "We're here to meet our Maker y'know."

"You what?" she says.

"We're here to meet our Maker," repeated old Billy.

"Meet your Maker . . . meet your Maker," she says, "what on Earth d'you mean by that?"

"You know the verse as well as I do," says old Billy, "when two or three are gathered together in my name," said the Lord, "I shall be there in the mist."

"Mist?" she says, "mist? Oh no no no, Puddick, you mean midst."

"No I don't," says old Billy, "I mean mist." And pointing over across the Common he said in a croaky voice, "Look over there! Look over there! Here he comes now!" And well she might have looked, because from where she sat on her seat high up in her pony and trap, she could just make out the unmistakeable figure of an unearthly being, covered all over from head to toe in a shimmering white shroud, moving very slowly towards the churchyard – pushing a wheelbarrer!

Well, whether or not she had any desire to meet her Maker then, or whether she wus just frightened near to death, we shall never know, because with one almighty ear-splitting scream, she hollered out, "I ain't ready to meet him yet! I ain't ready to meet him yet!" And then, whipping up her little old pony, she disappeared at a considerable rate of knots across the Common, a'shouting and a'hollering at the top of her voice – just as old Percy Lamkin appeared through the gloom, covered all over with one of them there lillywhite flour bags out of Charley Buckley's windmill, that looked for all the world like a ghostly white shroud, what he'd put on over his head for the purpose of keeping out all that damp and misty cold – pushing his wheelbarrer! . . .

. . . "Y'know," says old Billy, as the three of us pushed our barrers through the now unimpeded churchyard gates, "that most definitely was, without a shadow of doubt, one of the bestest examples of divine intervention you are ever likely to see!"

Well, we did laugh over that y'know, and that still makes me laugh even to this very day.

Ha, I told you that the churchyard gates very rarely gets unlocked just for the one, didn't I? But Old Percy Lamkin summed it all up y'know.

"Ha ha ha," chortled old Billy, as all three of us were passing through the seldom unlocked churchyard gates, "that ain't very often you see three old bodies going through these 'ere gates under their own steam all at the same time is it?"

"No," says Percy Lamkin, "and that ain't very often you'll see 'em all walking out again neither!" Well, we had to laugh!

And so, with that sobering thought in mind, after we had finished the job, we went down to the Rose and Crown to celebrate!

Well, that's all we got time for now. I hope you've enjoyed a'listening to these little stories as much as I've enjoyed telling them. I shall have to be off now, that's getting late. What's that you say? Do I wants a lift? No – I've got stairs in my little old cottage – oh! – I see – do I wants a ride home? Well, that's very civil of you . . .

Goodnight all . . .

Footnote

IN RECENT YEARS, the Rose and Crown has undergone major refurbishments. As a result, both the rounded bottomed fire bucket (as in 'The Buckland Common Bucket Brigade') and the Shroud (as in 'Dawdling Bugs, Dung Clamps and Things that go Bump in the Night') are no longer displayed. They are, however, along with other artefacts, now in a place of safe keeping – at least, that's how the story goes . . . !

The Christmas Produce Fair referred to in 'The Parable of the Five-pence Ha'penny Talent' has never taken place – as far as can be ascertained – during any living memory. The conundrum is therefore – has there ever been one? – will we ever know? – all of which brings us back full circle to the question in the Preface . . . are they authentic country tales – or are they just a figment of the storyteller's imagination . . .

. . . Does it really matter?

List of Illustrations

by Elspeth Yule